CODE OF PRACTICE
FOR
PROJECT
~~MANAGEMENT~~
FOR CONSTRUCTION
AND DEVELOPMENT

CODE OF PRACTICE
FOR
PROJECT MANAGEMENT
FOR CONSTRUCTION
AND DEVELOPMENT

The
CHARTERED INSTITUTE OF BUILDING

First published 1992

© The Chartered Institute of Building 1992

Project Management Agreement and Conditions of Engagement Guidance Note and Memorandum is reproduced with the permission of The Royal Institution of Chartered Surveyors who own the copyright.

ISBN 1-85380-057-0

A CIP record for this book is available from the British Library

Designed and Produced by
Chase Production Services
Chase House, Chalford Oaks, Chipping Norton, Oxon OX7 5QR
for the publishers
The Chartered Institute of Building
Englemere, Kings Ride, Ascot, Berks SL5 8BJ

Printed in Great Britain

FOREWORD

Many of the construction industry's influential Clients are turning to Project Management as the most effective way to procure a new facility, whether it be a multi-storey office block, an aircraft hangar or a cable stayed bridge. This Code is a key work of guidance and reference, compiled under the active direction of a multi-disciplinary Project Team.

Project Management, as a professional discipline, has been the subject of numerous definitions and considerable confusion in the construction industry. The aim of this Code of Practice is to provide Clients and all members of the construction team with a definitive strategy for any project from the outset, defining the responsibilities of all concerned to ensure completion on time, to the specification defined by the brief and within budget.

The team assembled to create the Code included all the recognised professional institutions within the industry and has been accepted as a definitive document which will enable a Client to understand the role and responsibilities of the project manager on any major scheme.

The Code is also a practical document and will allow those anxious to practice the art to gain an understanding of the processes involved and techniques employed. Similarly, students will be able to explore the complete perspective of Project Management activity.

The Code recognises that each project is unique and that the means by which it may be procured will be subject to variation. The specimen forms, charts and checklists cannot be regarded as appropriate for universal application – they are only examples and their value must be assessed for the project in question.

The structure of the Code mirrors generally the Project Management process itself. Each chapter deals with the specific phase of Project Management and is supported by specimen forms, checklists and examples of typical documentation.

The key issues considered are under the headings of Feasibility, Strategy, Pre-Construction, Construction, Fitting Out, Commissioning, Completion and Handover, and Occupation.

The final task for the Project Manager is to make a thorough assessment of all elements of the project and to draw out for the benefit of the Client and the Project Management practice any lessons which can be applied to future projects.

At Part 2 is the Project Management Agreement and Conditions of Engagement which is reproduced by the kind permission of the Royal Institution of Chartered Surveyors. The use of the Agreement is endorsed by those who contributed to the production of this Code. The Code is completed by a typical Project Handbook included at Part 3.

ACKNOWLEDGEMENTS

In January 1991 the Chartered Institute of Building hosted an interdisciplinary forum on Project Management at its headquarters in Ascot.

The outcome of this meeting was the formation of a Working Group with no specific terms of reference other than to discuss matters of mutual interest and to identify areas of common concern.

It was established, at a very early stage, that a great deal of confusion surrounded the term 'Project Management' especially among the industry's Clients and that there was a need for a document which clearly defined this rapidly developing discipline.

Hence, the idea of a Code of Practice was born.

The composition of the Working Group was:

F A Hammond MSc Tech CEng
MICE FCIOB MAmorSCE FBIM — Chairman

G S Ayres FRICS FCIArb FFB — Royal Institution of Chartered Surveyors

R J Cecil DipArch RIBA FRSA — Royal Institute of British Architects

D K Doran BSc Eng DIC FCGI
CEng FICE FIStructE — Institution of Structural Engineers

R Elliott CEng MICE — Institution of Civil Engineers

D J Gillingham CEng FCIBSE — Chartered Institution of Building Services Engineers

R J Biggs MSc FCIOB MBIM MAPM

Professor N Fisher PhD
MSc MCIOB

J C B Goring BSc (Hons)
MCIOB MAPM

D P Horne FCIOB FFB FBIM

P K Smith MCIOB

R A Waterhouse MSc MCIOB
MBIM MSIB MAPM

S R Witkowski MSc (Eng) — Consultant

P B Cullimore FCIOB ARICS
MASI MBIM — Secretary

Contributions were also received from the Association of Project Managers and the British Property Federation.

This Document is the result of interdisciplinary co-operation between the professions within the construction/property industry. It represents a major step towards producing better controlled, co-ordinated, efficient and effective teams capable of responding and providing total satisfaction to the industry's Clients.

On behalf of the Chartered Institute of Building I would like to express my sincere appreciation to all the members of the Working Group who have given so freely of their time and experience.

I know that I speak for all of us on the Working Group in acknowledging the major part played by Richard Witkowski who had the unenviable task of co-ordinating the many contributions into this one document.

We acknowledge with grateful thanks the right to include the Project Management Agreement and Conditions of Engagement which are reproduced with the permission of The Royal Institution of Chartered Surveyors who own the copyright. The Guidance Notes were prepared jointly by the Royal Institution of Chartered Surveyors and the Project Management Association of the RICS.

Our thanks also to Peter Harlow, the CIOB Information Resource Centre Manager for his assistance at the publication stage.

The CIOB is grateful to the Directors of Project Management International Plc for assistance in the preparation of this Code and to the many other organisations who have kindly allowed us to reproduce extracts of their own documentation.

This co-operation is gratefully acknowledged.

F A Hammond
Chairman

CONTENTS

CONTENTS

PART 3.
PROJECT HANDBOOK

LIST OF FIGURES AND APPENDICES

Aftercare Engineer: The Aftercare Engineer provides a support service to the Client/user during the initial 6–12 months of occupancy and is, therefore, most likely a member of the commissioning team.

Brief: Defines the Client's objectives, budget, and functional requirements for the proposed facility.

Client: Owner and/or developer of the facility; in some cases the ultimate user.

Consultants: Advisors to the Client and the Project Team at the pre-development, construction and handover stages of the facility.

Contractor(s): Generally applied to:

(a) the main contractor responsible for the total construction and completion process

or

(b) two or more contractors responsible under separate contractual provisions for major or high technology parts of a very complex facility.

(Refer also to sub-contractor).

Construction Supervisor: the person concerned with only a specific phase, or works of the project, eg clerk of works or resident engineer.

Commissioning Team:
(a) Client commissioning: predominantly the Client's personnel assisted by the contractor and members of the Professional Team.

(b) Engineering services commissioning: Specialist contractor(s) and equipment manufacturer(s) monitored by the main contractor and Professional Team members concerned.

Design Team: Architect(s), engineers and technology specialists responsible for the conceptual design aspects and their development into drawings, specifications and instructions required for construction of the facility and associated processes.

Development surveyor: Provides information and advice on the environmental planning implications of proposed facility, eg economic, social, financial and population trends.

Design freeze: Completion and Client's final approval of the design and associated processes, ie no further changes are contemplated or accepted within the budget approved in the brief.

Design audit: Carried out by members of an independent design team providing confirmation or otherwise that the project design meets, in the best possible way, the Client's brief and objective.

Facility: All types of constructions, eg buildings, shopping malls, terminals, hospitals, hotels, sporting/leisure centres, industrial/ processing/ chemical plants and installations, highways and other infrastructure projects.

Facilities management: Planning, organisation and managing physical assets and their related support services in a cost effective way to give the optimum return on investment in both financial and quality terms.

Feasibility stage: Initial project development and planning carried out by assessing the Client's objectives and providing advice and expertise in order to help the Client define more precisely what is needed and how it can be achieved.

Handbook: *see* Project Handbook.

Life cycle costing: Establishes the present value of the total cost of an asset over its operating life for the purpose of comparison with alternatives available. This enables investment options to be more effectively evaluated and decisions made.

Master Programme/Project Master Development Programme:

Overall statement of the project approved plan and its stages, presented in a graphical form.

Occupation: Sometimes referred to as 'migration' or 'decanting'. It is the actual process of physical movement (transfer) and placement of personnel (employees) into their new working environment of the facility.

Professional Team: Design Team and consultants.

Project Team: Design Team, consultants, contractors and sub-contractors.

Project Handbook: Guide to the Project Team members in the performance of their duties, identifying their responsibilities and detailing the various activities and procedures (often referred to as the 'project bible').

Risk factor: Is associated with the anticipation and reduction of the effects of risk and problems by a pro-active approach to project development and planning.

Strategy stage: During this stage a sound basis is created for the Client on which decisions can be made allowing the project to proceed to completion. It provides a framework for the effective execution of the project.

Sub-contractor: Contractor(s) who undertake specialist work within the project and known as 'specialist', 'works', 'trade', 'work package', and 'labour only'.

Tenant: Facility user who is generally not the Client or the developer.

User: The ultimate occupier of the facility.

PART 1.

PROJECT MANAGEMENT

1. INTRODUCTION

PROJECT MANAGEMENT

Project Management is one of a number of options open to a Client for the procurement of a construction project. It has a long history but in its modern form its use for construction only extends back for as little as 20–30 years. Much of the earlier codification of the principles and practices of Project Management was developed in the US, although the Chartered Institute of Building published its seminal work on the subject in 1979.

Project Management may be defined as *the overall planning, control and co-ordination of a project from inception to completion aimed at meeting a Client's requirements in order that the project will be completed on time within authorised cost and to the required quality standards.*

This Code of Practice is the authoritative guide and reference to the principles and practice of Project Management in construction and development. It will be of value to Clients, Project Management practices and educational establishments/students and to the construction industry in general. Much of the information contained in the Code will also be relevant to Project Management operating in other industrial spheres.

Irrespective of the procurement path selected, the Client's objective will be *to obtain a totally functional facility.*

The Project Manager, both acting on behalf of, and representing the Client has the duty of *providing a cost effective and independent service correlating, integrating and managing different disciplines and expertise, to satisfy the objectives and provisions of the project brief from inception to completion. The service provided must be to the Client's satisfaction, safeguard his interests at all times, and, where possible, give consideration to the needs of the eventual user of the facility.*

In his dealings with the Project Team the Project Manager has an obligation to recognise and respect the professional codes of the other disciplines and in particular, the responsibilities of all disciplines to society, the environment and each other.

There are differences in the levels of responsibility, authority and job title of the individual responsible for the project, and the terms Project Manager, Project Co-ordinator and Project Administrator are used.

It is essential that, in ensuring an effective and cost conscious service, the project should be under the direction and control of a competent practitioner with a proven Project Management 'track record' developed from a construction industry related professional discipline. This person is designated the *Project Manager* and is to be appointed by the Client with full responsibility for the project. Having delegated powers at inception, the Project Manager will exercise, in the closest association with the *Project Team*, an executive role throughout the project.

A typical job specification for a Project Manager is given at Appendix 1.1. It will be subject to modifications to reflect the Client's objectives, the nature of the project and contractual requirements.

A *Supervising Officer* and/or *Contract Administrator* may be appointed for the construction and subsequent stages of the project. This post is often taken by a member of the Professional Team who will have a direct contractual responsibility to the Client, subject to consultation with the Project Manager.

The term *Project Co-ordinator* is applied where the responsibility and authority embrace only part of the project, eg pre-construction, construction and handover/migration stages.

A matrix correlating typical Project Management duties and Client's requirements is given at Figure 1.1.

Under the overall direction and supervision of a Project Manager, projects are usually carried out by a Project Team viz.

- Design Team: architect(s); structural/civil/M&E engineers and technology specialists.

- Consultants, covering: quantity surveying, development surveying, planning, legal issues, finance/leasing, insurances, design audit, health, safety and environmental protection, facilities management, and highways/traffic planning.

- Contractor(s) and sub-contractor(s)

An organisation structure for Project Management is shown in Figure 1.2.

The organisation structure shown in Figure 1.2. is idealised and in practice there will be many variants, responding to the nature of the project, the contractual arrangements, type of Project Management (external or in-house) involved, and above all, the Client's requirements.

Effective Project Management must, at all times, fully embrace all provisions for quality assurance and health, safety and environmental protection.

These aspects are to be considered as incorporated and implied in all relevant activities specified in this Code.

The major stages of a project and their inter-relationship are shown in Figure 1.3.

Figure 1.1. Typical Project Manager's duties

DUTIES These vary between projects, relevant responsibilities and authority.	CLIENT'S REQUIREMENTS			
	In-House Project Management		Independent Project Management	
	Project Management	Project Co-ordination	Project Management	Project Co-ordination
Be party to the contract	●		+	
Assist in preparing the Client's brief	●		●	
Develop Project Manager's brief	●		●	
Advise on budget/funding arrangements	●		+	
Advise on site acquisition, grants and planning	●		+	
Arrange feasibility study and report	●	+	●	+
Develop project strategy	●	+	●	+
Prepare Project Handbook	●	+	●	+
Develop consultants' briefs	●	+	●	+
Devise project programme	●	+	●	+
Select project team members	●	+	+	+
Establish management structure	●	+	●	+
Co-ordinate design processes	●	+	●	+
Appoint consultants	●		●	
Arrange insurance and warranties	●	●	●	+
Select procurement system	●	●	●	+
Arrange tender documentation	●	●	●	+
Organise contractor pre-qualification	●	●	●	+
Evaluate tenders	●	●	●	+
Participate in contractor selection	●	●	●	+
Participate in contractor appointment	●	●	●	+
Organise control systems	●	●	●	●
Monitor progress	●	●	●	●
Arrange meetings	●	●	●	●
Authorise payments	●	●	●	+
Organise communication/reporting systems	●	●	●	●
Provide total co-ordination	●	●	●	●
Issue safety/health procedures	●	●	●	●
Address environmental aspects	●	●	●	●
Co-ordinate statutory authorities	●	●	●	●
Monitor budget and variation orders	●	●	●	●
Develop final account	●	●	●	●
Arrange pre-commissioning/commissioning	●	●	●	●
Organise handover/occupation	●	●	●	●
Advise on marketing/disposal	●	+	●	+
Organise maintenance manuals	●	●	●	+
Plan for maintenance period	●	●	●	+
Develop maintenance programme/staff training	●	●	●	+
Plan facilities management	●	●	●	+
Arrange for feedback monitoring	●	●	●	+

Legend: ● = typical duties   + = possible additional duties

Figure 1.2 Project Management organisation structure

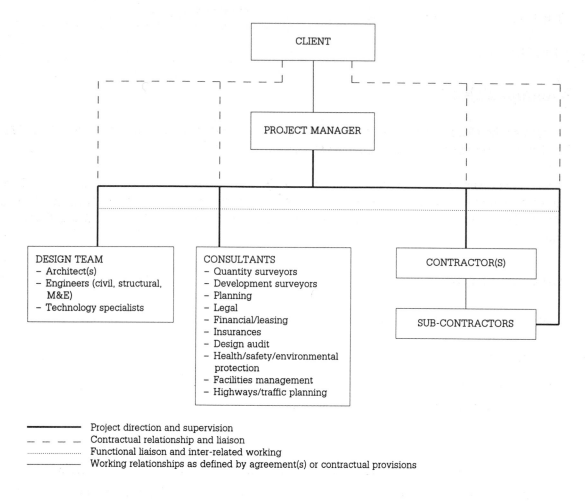

```
Project direction and supervision
Contractual relationship and liaison
Functional liaison and inter-related working
Working relationships as defined by agreement(s) or contractual provisions
```

Figure 1.3 Major elements of a construction project and their inter-relationships

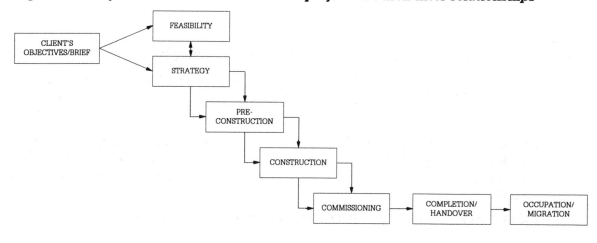

APPENDIX 1.1 TYPICAL JOB SPECIFICATION

Job Title: Project Manager

Date Effective:

General objective

Acting as the Client's representative within the contractual terms applicable, to direct, co-ordinate and supervise the project in association with the Project Team.

The Project Manager will ensure that the Client's brief, all designs, specifications and relevant information/data are made available to, and are executed as specified with due regard to cost, by the Design Team, consultants and contractors, (ie the Project Team), so that the Client's objectives are fully met.

Relationships

Responsible and Reporting to: The Client

Subordinates:

— Practice support staff, eg planning, financial.
— secretarial/clerical staff.

Functional:

— Fully integrated working with any project support staff who are not line subordinates.
— Liaison, as required/expedient with relevant Client's staff, eg legal, insurance, taxation.
— Full interdependent co-operation with:

(a) Design Team and consultants (Professional Team);

(b) Contractor(s).

External:

— Liaison with local or other relevant authority on matters concerning the project.
— Contact with suppliers of construction materials/equipment, in order to be aware of the most efficient and cost-effective application, and working methods.
— Contact with:

(a) Client's Information Technology (IT) team or other higher technology sources, able to provide expertise on the application of advanced technology in the design and/or construction processes of the project (eg communications, environment, security and fire prevention/ protection systems);

(b) and preferably, membership of appropriate professional bodies/societies.

Authority

The Project Manager has responsibility for approving:

a) costs (limit agreed with Client) re-allocation within the capital or sectional budget for modifications/rectifications that are necessary or more effective and are agreed with the Design Team, consultants and contractor(s);

b) expenditure from the project's petty cash (limit agreed with Client) for stationery and routine office expenses;

c) special working conditions, overtime and personal expenses of subordinate staff;

The Project Manager will also have the authority to:

— authorise, in consultation with the Client, purchase of site office equipment and materials, at the commencement and throughout the project;

— incur personal expenditure and expenditure associated with visitors' hospitality/entertainment, within limits approved by the Client;

— sign relevant project documentation/certification/variations and correspondence.

Detailed responsibilities and duties

Analysis of the Client's objectives and requirements, assessment of their feasibility and assistance in the completion of project brief and establishment of the capital budget.

Formulation, for the Client's approval, of the strategic plan for achieving the stated objectives within the budget, including, where applicable, the quality assurance scheme.

Generally keeping the Client informed, throughout the project, on progress and problems, design/budgeting/construction variations, and such other matters considered to be relevant.

Participation in:

— making recommendations to the Client and, if required, in:
  a) the selection of the Professional Team as well as in the negotiation of their terms and conditions of engagement;
  b) the appointment of contractors/sub-contractors, including the giving of advice on the most suitable forms of tender and contract.

Preparation for the Client's approval of:

a) the overall project programme embracing site acquisition, relevant investigations, planning, pre-design, design, construction and handover/occupation stages;

b) proposals for architectural and engineering services. The Project Manager will monitor progress and initiate appropriate action on all submissions concerned with planning approvals and statutory requirements (viz timely submission, alternative proposals and necessary waivers);

c) the project budget and relevant cash flows, giving due consideration to matters likely to affect the viability of the project development;

Finalisation of the Client's brief and its confirmation to the Professional Team. Providing them with all existing and, if necessary, any supplementary data on surveys, site investigations, adjoining owners, adverse rights or restrictions and site accessibility/traffic constraints.

Recommending to the Client and securing approval for any modifications or variations to the agreed brief, approved designs, programmes and/or budgets resulting from Professional Team discussions and reviews.

Setting up the management and administrative structure for the project and thereby defining:

— responsibilities and duties, as well as lines of reporting, for all parties;

— procedures for clear and efficient communication;

— systems and procedures for issuing instructions, drawings, certificates, schedules and valuations and the preparation and submission of reports and relevant documentary returns.

Agreeing tendering strategy with the Professional Team.

Advising the Client as necessary on:

— the progress of the Professional Team and the production of required drawings/information and tender documents, stressing at all times the need for a cost-effective approach to optimise costs in construction methods, subsequent maintenance requirements, preparation of tender documents and performance/workmanship warranties;

— the correctness of tender documents;

— the prospective tenderers pre-qualified by the Professional Team, obtaining additional information if pertinent and confirming accepted tenders to the Client and the Team;

— the preliminary construction programme for the main contractor(s), agreeing any revisions to meet fully the Client's requirements and releasing this to the Project Team for action;

— the progress of all elements of the project, especially adherence to the agreed capital and sectional budgets, as well as meeting the set standards and initiating any remedial action;

— the contractual activities the Client must undertake, including user study groups and approval/decision points;

Establishing with the quantity surveyor the cost monitoring and reporting system and providing feedback to the Professional Team and Client on budget status and cash-flow.

Organising and/or participating in:

— presentations to the Client, with advice on and securing approval for the detailed design of fabrics, finishes, fitting-out work and the environment of major interior spaces;

— all meetings with the Project Team and others involved in the project (chairing or acting as Secretary) to ensure:

a) an adequate supply of information/data to all concerned;

b) that progress is in accordance with the programme;

c) that costs are within the budget(s);

d) that required standards and specifications are achieved;

e) that contractors have adequate resources for the management, supervision and quality control of the project;

f) that the relevant members of the Project Team inspect and supervise construction stages as specified by the contract(s).

Responsible for:

— preparation of the Project Handbook;

— achieving good communications and motivating all personnel;

— monitoring progress, costs and quality and initiating action to rectify any variations;

— setting priorities and effective management of time;

— co-ordinating the Project Team's activities and output;

— monitoring project resources against planned levels and initiating necessary remedial action;

— preparing and presenting specified reports to the Client;

— submitting to the Client time sheets and other data on costing and control processes, including required returns and all other relevant information;

— approving, in collaboration with the Project Team and within the building contract provisions, any sub-let work;

— identifying any existing or potential problems, disputes or conflicts and resolving them, with the co-operation of all concerned in the best interests of the Client;

— recommending to the Client consultants' interim payment applications and monitoring such applications from contractors;

— monitoring all pre-commissioning checks and progress of any remedial defects liability work and the release of retention monies;

— verifying with the Project Team members concerned any claims for extensions of time or additional payments and advising the Client accordingly;

— checking Professional Team's final accounts prior to payment by the Client;

— monitoring the preparation of contractors' final accounts, obtaining relevant certificates and submitting them for settlement by the Client;

— ensuring the inclusion in the contract and subsequently requesting the Design Team, consultants and contractors to supply the Client with as-built and installed drawings, operating and maintenance manuals, as well as ensuring arrangements are made for effective training of the Client's engineering and maintenance staff, ie facilities management.

Taking all appropriate steps to ensure that site contractors and other regular or casual workers observe all the rules, regulations and practices of safety and fire prevention/protection. Exercising 'good site housekeeping' at all times.

Participating in the final reconciliation of the project and taking such action as directed or required.

Non-contractual responsibilities

Participating in informal discussions with own and other practices, as well as the Client's staff, on technical details, methods of operations, problem solving and any other pertinent action(s) relevant to present or previous projects, in order to exchange views/knowledge conducive to providing a more effective overall performance.

The Project Manager has responsibility for:

a) personnel matters relating to subordinates, including staff appraisal/reviews, training/development and job coaching and counselling, as defined by the Client and/or Project Management practice guidelines and procedures;

b) updating self and subordinates in new ideas relating to Project Management, including management/supervisory skills and practice generally, business, financial and economic trends, the latest forms of contract, planning and Building Regulations, as well as advances in construction techniques, plant and equipment.

2. FEASIBILITY

Project Management starts by gaining an understanding of the Client's* objectives and by providing the expertise to allow the Client to define more precisely what is needed and how it can be achieved. In this way Project Management can influence the decisions on the type of facility required, its use, user needs, architectural concepts, construction time scale and cost criteria. The Client can also be guided around such obstacles as unavailability of relevant project resourcing, and be advised, for example, on how to 'buy best', to develop existing facilities, to consider alternative locations, to evaluate materials and construction methods, as well as being advised of potential costs involved in overcoming specific problems.

In consequence the recognition and control of risk is critical. All projects go through the two distinct phases. First, feasibility, involving site acquisition and its conditions, financial viability, funding, grants, taxation, pre-letting, planning permissions and the 'what if' factors, and, secondly, commitment. The objective of Project Management is to anticipate and reduce the effect of risk, rather than dealing with it as it arises.

Figure 2.1. illustrates the relationship throughout the project between the 'scope for change' and the 'cost of change'.

These considerations assist the Client in establishing a comprehensive project brief, which highlights the parameters of cost, time, quality, facility function and specifies the contractual aspects and applicable agreements. The importance of the brief cannot be over-emphasised, as it constitutes the basic reference document for the project and is a formal specific expression of what is required from the project. Therefore, the client must commit adequate time and resources to its preparation. The brief should be subject only to minimal changes once the detailed design commences. It must give sufficient details and enough information to allow the Professional Team (Design Team and consultants) to finalise conceptual design, (*see* Figure 2.2).

At this stage the Client and the prospective Project Manager meet and agree:

— the bases for the feasibility and strategy stages;

— an outline Master Programme and cost plan;

— a subsequent action plan for the project;

— the terms and timing for the appointment of the Project Manager. (At Part 2 is the RICS recommended Agreement and Conditions of Engagement.)

---

*'The Client' may be an organisation consisting of individuals and departments who have different subjective views of requirements. In such cases Project Management would:
— get to know the key people concerned and assess how their roles and personal objectives may attempt to influence the feasibility stage study;
— help them to come to a common agreement by collaborative action.

Figure 2.1 Relationship between 'scope for change' and 'cost of change'

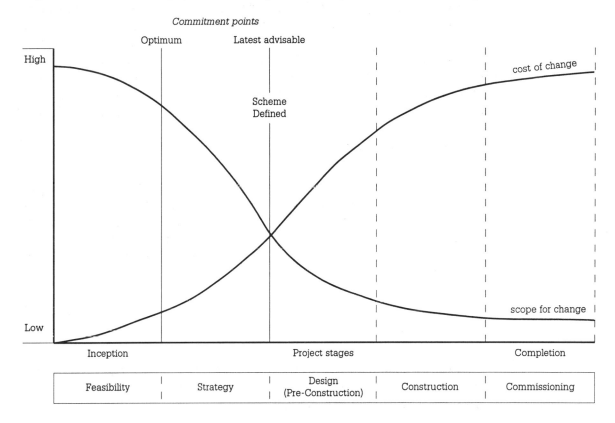

Figure 2.2 Establishing the Client brief

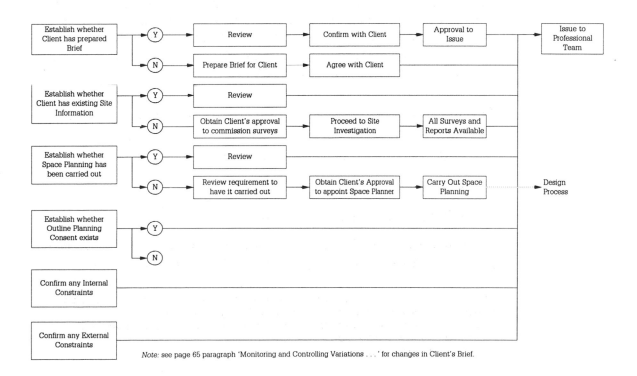

Note: see page 65 paragraph 'Monitoring and Controlling Variations . . .' for changes in Client's Brief.

Other services which might be offered at this time to assist the Client include:

— reviewing and participating in the drafting of legal and financial documents to check on the consistency of definitions and terminology. This would include an assessment of legal issues relating to:
  contracts;
  land (conditions/constraints relevant to 'ground landlord' and site);
  financial arrangements, insurances and taxation;
  tenant(s) agreements (if applicable)

— investigating planning/statutory authority approvals and the outline strategy for implementation;

— the valuation and acquisition of land for the project;

— preliminary assessment of the cost/value of the facility (type of building/ construction and standards of finish), including life cycle costing method, in order to evaluate more effectively finance and design options (eg, an increase in initial outlay may result in a significant reduction in 'operating' costs). This would include an input from a facilities management consultant (*see* Appendix 2.1).

— initiating first cost plan/budget limits and cash flow forecasts;

— developing finance options and negotiating on funding;

— identifying Professional Team members and deciding the basis of their appointment;

— preparing terms of reference/conditions for the members of the Professional Team essential for the feasibility studies and their selection/appointment. (*See* Figure 2.3 and Appendices 2.2 and 2.3.);

— monitoring the Professional Team's studies/work against the programme and cost plan;

— co-ordinating the preparation of the feasibility report and recommendations;

— reaching a decision about project viability based on the report and recommendations.

Figure 2.3 *Selection and appointment of Professional Team members*

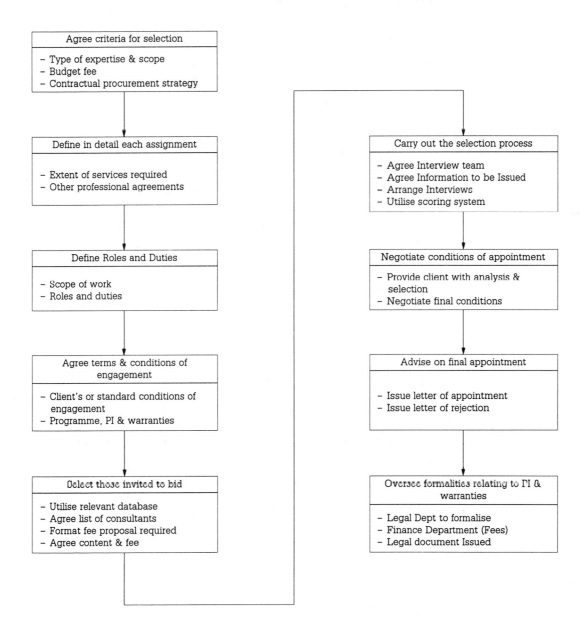

APPENDIX 2.1 FACILITIES MANAGEMENT OUTLINE

1. Facilities management embraces planned maintenance of property, plant and machinery, with the wider objective of achieving the optimum usage of property and its assets.

2. Its justification arises from the ever changing ratio of labour, material and asset costs attributable to any item of commercial activity.

3. Using computer aided design (CAD), a drawing of each building/facility is created to serve as the key and over which layers of information are stored: such layers are capable of switching on and off at will and are interactive with the database. This, in effect, provides a user friendly visual index to the system enabling all databases to be driven from a visual reference point.

4. The system replaces conventional record drawings and maintenance/operational manuals, having the facility to provide print-outs of specific areas or plant as and when required. Such print-outs can be used, lost or thrown away, without affecting the viability of the system.

5. Information recorded assists in the execution of annual energy audits.

6. Term maintenance requirements can be incorporated from which contracts can be initiated and cost and quality controlled, through the provision of print out work sheets requiring completion and return for checking and updating.

7. Facilities management collates, analyses and extrapolates all relevant cost information regarding the assets under management, enabling budgetary control to be perfected and costs to be related more directly.

8. Space planning and space costing, so important to any building/facility user, are better appreciated and regulated using the CAD facility.

9. The monitoring of cash flow variances increases the accuracy of budget forecasting.

10. The movement of assets within and between buildings/facilities are tracked, replacing the conventional inventory with pro-active CAD database, that locates and logs each asset, thereby assisting with the identification of vandalism and theft.

11. Facilities management prolongs the effective life of assets by braking the rate and timing of decline.

12. Most importantly facilities management programmes can now be accommodated on relatively inexpensive personal computers enabling dissemination through user friendly visually indexed information to local management within each property, thus facilitating the updating of the system through 'hands on' control.

13. The system can be as basic or as complex as the Client's requirements dictate and once established can be extended as required, thus enabling budgetary control and careful research coupled with a learning curve to be accommodated.

Facilities management, through its various functions, enables management to relate specifically the implication of changes in market forces on capital assets, thereby giving tighter control of budgets and overheads.

APPENDIX 2.2
SELECTION AND APPOINTMENT OF PROFESSIONAL TEAM MEMBERS

1. Determine what duties are to be assumed by the members and prepare a schedule of responsibilities. If applicable, consider what level of in-house expertise is available.

2. Check to see if the Client has any in-house procedures or standard conditions of engagement for the appointment of members and what scope there is for deviating from these.

3. Decide on the qualities most needed for the project, and the method of appointment. Agree these with the Client.

4. Establish criteria for evaluating members with weighting values (eg 5 vital, 0 unimportant) for each criterion. (*See* Assessment Sheet.)

5. Assemble a list of candidates from references and recommendations. Check any in-house approved and updated lists of consultants.

6. Prepare a shortlist by gathering information about possible candidate(s). Check which firms or individuals are prepared, in principle, to submit a proposal.

7. Assess candidates against general criteria and invite proposals from a select number (no more than six or less than three per position). Invitation documents should be prepared in accordance with the checklist given below. Competitive fee bids, if required, should conform to relevant codes of practice.

8. Arrange for conditions of engagement to be drawn up. The conditions, the form of which will vary with the work required and the type of Client, should refer to a schedule of responsibilities for the stages for which the member is appointed and include a clause dictating compliance with the Project Handbook. The conditions of engagement should be based as closely as possible on industry standards (eg as set by the RIBA, ACE and RICS). Consistency of style and structure between conditions for different members of the team will improve each member's understanding of their own and others' responsibilities. Each set should include this aspect. Fee calculation and payment terms should be clearly defined at the outset, together with the treatment of expenses, ie included or not in the agreed fee.

9. Determine the criteria for assessing the members' proposals. Agree these with the Client.

10. Appraise the proposals and select the candidate(s) most appropriate for the project. Proposals should be analysed against the agreed criteria using weighting analysis.

11. Arrange final interview with selected candidates (minimum of two) for final selection/negotiation as necessary. (*See* Appendix 2.3.)

12. Submit a report and recommendation to the Client.

13. Selected member appointed by Client.

14. Unsuccessful candidates notified that an appointment has been made.

Checklist

Invitation documents must include:

- A schedule of responsibilities.

- The form of interview panel.

- Draft conditions of engagement (an indication of the type to be used).

- Design skills or expertise required.

- Personnel who will work on the project, their roles, timescales, commitment, output.

- Warranties required, for whose benefit and in what terms.

Invitations should ask candidate(s) to include information on the level of current professional indemnity insurance cover for the duration of the project. Details of policy, date of expiry and extent of cover for sub-contracted services must be provided.

APPENDIX 2.3 ASSESSMENT SHEET
SELECTION AND APPOINTMENT OF PROFESSIONAL TEAM/ CONTRACTORS

CLIENT   APPOINTMENT

INTERVIEWING PANEL: DATE:

Criteria or Expertise required	Action Looked For (how demonstrated)	W	Evidence expected by Panel	R	Weight × Rating
1.					
2.					
3.					
4.					
5.					
6.					
7.					
8.					
9.					
10.					

General Observations

W = Weighting – out of 5

R = Rating of evidence
Very strong	4
Strong	3
Adequate	2
Inadequate	1

3. STRATEGY

Distinction between the tasks and activities of the feasibility and strategy stages is not always clear, as each is influenced to a certain extent by the considerations and findings of the other. Feedback (illustrated in Figure 1.2) is essential in order to establish for the Client a sound basis for decision-making at the conceptual phases of the project and, subsequently, for its effective execution.

It is at the strategy stage that the Client formally appoints the Project Manager to exercise the co-ordinating, monitoring and controlling role for the project and its satisfactory completion in accordance with the brief.

A typical strategy stage consists of the main elements shown in Figure 3.1.

Figure 3.1 Elements of the strategy stage

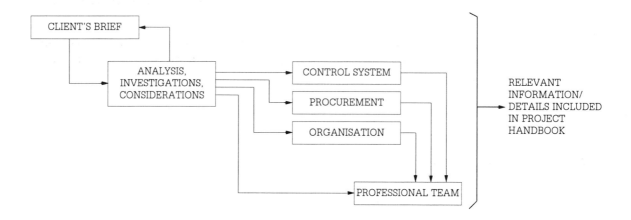

STRATEGY OUTLINE AND DEVELOPMENT

- Reviewing the project brief with the Client and existing members of the Professional Team to ascertain that the Client's objectives have been met. Preparing a final version in written form.

- Establishing, in consultation with the Client and Professional Team members, a project management structure (organisation) and the participants' roles and responsibilities, including access to Client and related communication routes, and 'decision required' points. (*See* Project Handbook for details)

- Establishing that 'value management' is applied effectively from the earliest stages of the preparation of the design brief until the design is complete. The emphasis will be on providing 'value for money' and in producing a facility that can be constructed at the lowest possible cost without reducing either scope or specifications. The design team and consultants should be encouraged not to accept conventional wisdom on what buildings/facilities cost, but consciously seek to reduce cost by better design and construction methods, ie the whole team 'designs in quality and drives out cost' at all stages in the design process.

- Advising the Client on the recruitment and appointment of additional consultants and design team members ie;

  — preparation and issue of selection/tender documentation;

  — evaluation, reporting and making recommendations;

  — assisting the Client in the preparation of agreements and in selection and appointment.

- Development and agreement of the most appropriate form of contract relative to the project objectives and the parameters of cost, time, quality and function.

- Determining whether certain activities, such as fitting out and occupation/ migration, constitute separate projects and should be treated as such. (*See* Figure 3.2.)

Figure 3.2 Contractual route

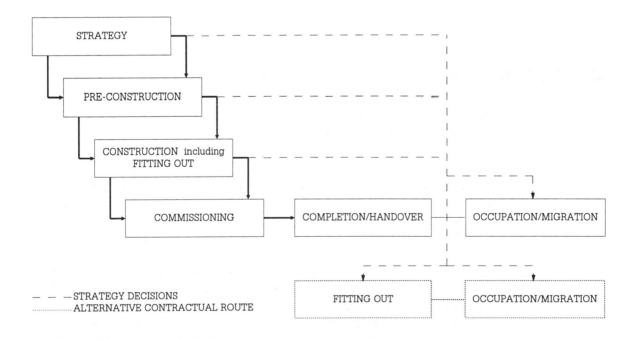

Site selection and acquisition

Site selection and acquisition is an important stage in the project cycle where the Client does not own the site to be developed. It should be effected as early as possible and, ideally, in parallel with the feasibility study. The work is carried out by a specialist consultant and monitored by the Project Manager. (*See* Figure 3.3.)

The objectives are to ensure that the requirements for the site are defined in terms of the facility to be constructed, that the selected site meets these requirements and that it is acquired within the constraints of the project programme.

To achieve these objectives the following tasks need to be carried out:

— preparing a statement of objectives/requirements for the site and facility/ buildings and agreeing this with the Client;

— preparing a specification for site selection and criteria for evaluating sites based on the objectives/requirements;

— establishing the outline funding arrangements;

— determining responsibilities within the Project Team (Client/Project Manager/commercial estate agent);

— appointing/briefing members of the team and developing programme for site selection and acquisition; monitoring and controlling progress against programme;

— actioning site searches and collecting data on sites against established criteria;

— evaluating sites against criteria and producing a short-list of three or four; agreeing weightings with Client;

— establishing initial outline designs and developing costs;

— discussing short-listed sites with relevant planning authorities;

— obtaining advice on approximate open market value of short-listed sites;

— selecting the site from a short-list;

— appointing agents for price negotiation and separate agents for independent valuation;

— appointing solicitors as appropriate;

— determining specific financial arrangements;

— exchanging contracts for site acquisition once terms are agreed.

Figure 3.3 Site selection and acquisition

Figure 3.3 Site selection and acquisition

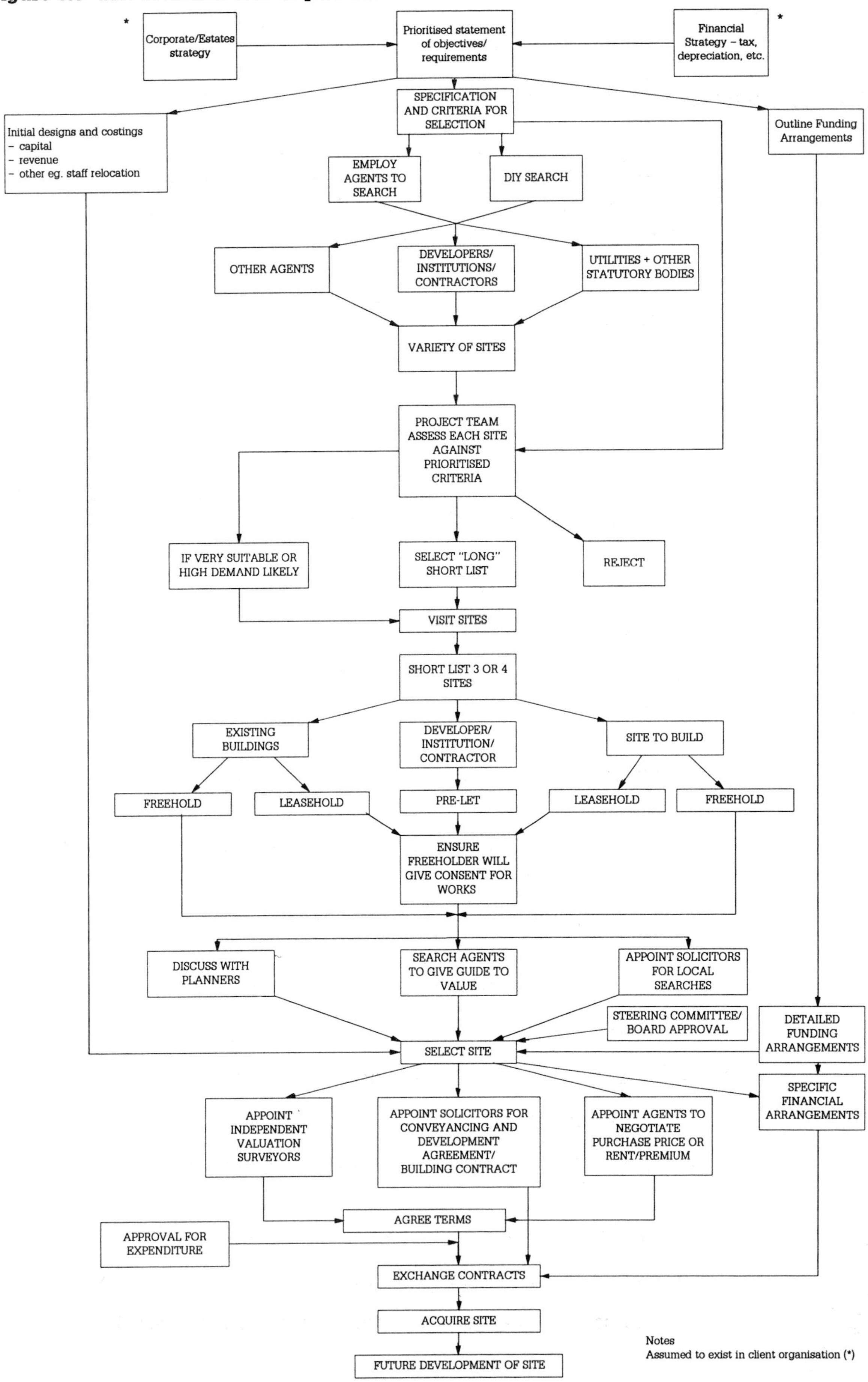

Notes
Assumed to exist in client organisation (*)

Site Investigation

The activities involved in a site investigation can be broadly grouped as shown in Figure 3.4. Certain of the tasks may overlap, depending on the level of expertise of the specialists appointed.

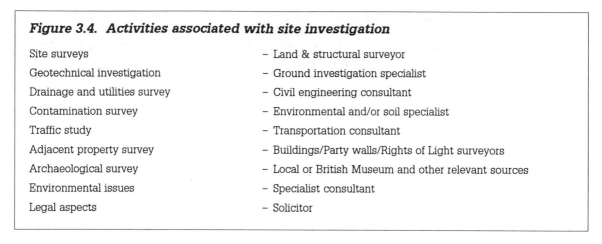

Figure 3.4. Activities associated with site investigation

Site surveys	– Land & structural surveyor
Geotechnical investigation	– Ground investigation specialist
Drainage and utilities survey	– Civil engineering consultant
Contamination survey	– Environmental and/or soil specialist
Traffic study	– Transportation consultant
Adjacent property survey	– Buildings/Party walls/Rights of Light surveyors
Archaeological survey	– Local or British Museum and other relevant sources
Environmental issues	– Specialist consultant
Legal aspects	– Solicitor

Confirmation that the tasks have been successfully completed is the responsibility of the Project Manager. Figure 3.5. illustrates the typical steps taken in a site investigation.

Figure 3.5 Site investigation

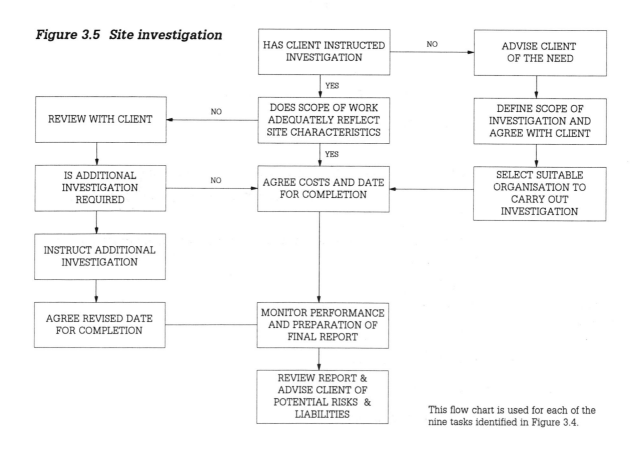

This flow chart is used for each of the nine tasks identified in Figure 3.4.

Each task can be broken down into a number of specific elements, viz

Site surveys
— location

— Ordnance Survey reference

— ground levels/contours

— physical features (eg roads, railways, rivers, ditches, trees, pylons, buildings, old foundations, erosion)

— existing boundaries

— adjacent properties

— site access

— structural survey

— previous use of site

Geotechnical investigation
— trial pits

— bore holes and bore hole logs

— geology of site including underground workings

— laboratory soil tests

— site tests

— ground water observation and pumping tests

— geophysical survey

Drainage and utilities survey
— existing site drainage (open ditch, culvert or piped system)

— extent of existing utilities on or nearest to the site (water, gas, electricity, telecoms)

— extent of any other services that may cross the site (eg Mercury/data lines, oil/fuel pipelines)

Contamination Survey
— asbestos

— methane

— toxic waste

— chemical tests

— radioactive substances

Traffic survey	— examination of traffic records from local authority
	— traffic counts
	— traffic patterns
	— computer simulation of existing traffic flows
	— delay analysis
	— noise levels
Adjacent property survey	— Right of Light
	— Party Wall agreements
	— schedule of conditions
	— foundations
	— drainage
	— access
	— public utilities serving the property
	— noise levels (eg airports, motorways, air conditioning equipment)
Archaeological survey	— examination of records
	— archaeological remains
Environmental issues	— effects of proposed development on local environment; environmental impact assessment, where appropriate
Legal aspects	— ownership of site
	— restrictive covenants
	— easements, eg Rights of Way, Rights of Light agreements
	— wayleaves
	— boundaries
	— Party Wall agreements
	— highways agreements
	— local authority agreements
	— air rights

PROJECT ORGANISATION AND CONTROL

A Project Management organisation structure sets out unambiguously and in detail (*see* Figure 1.2) how the parties to the project are to perform their functions in relation to each other in contributing to the overall scheme. It also identifies arrangements and procedures for monitoring and control and relevant administrative details. It is updated as circumstances dictate during the project lifetime and it should allow project objectives to be communicated and agreed by all concerned and promote effective team work.

Procedures covering relationships and arrangements for monitoring, control and administration should be developed, with the assistance of parties involved, for all stages of the project and cover time, costs, quality and reporting/decision making arrangements.

The organisation structure should identify clearly the involvement and obligations of the Client and his organisational backup.

Programmes

The various steps in the development of the project plan are shown in Figure 3.6. (Examples of typical programmes are given at Appendices 3.1 to 3.5)

The Master Programme should be developed and agreed with the Client and the members of the Professional Team concerned and detailed programmes for each stage of the project prepared as soon as the necessary parameters are established.

It is the Project Manager's responsibility to monitor the progress of the project against the Master and stage programmes and to initiate necessary action to rectify non-compliance.

Budget: Cost Plan and Cost Control

Cost plan

The objective of the cost plan is to provide the best estimate of the final cost of the project. The terms 'budget' and 'cost plan' are often regarded as synonymous. However, the difference is that 'budget' is the limit of expenditure defined for the project, whereas 'cost plan' is the plan of what the money will be spent on and when. The cost plan should, therefore, include the best possible estimate of the cash flow for the project and should also set targets for the future running costs of the facility. The cost plan should cover all stages of the project.

The method used to determine the budget will vary at different stages of the project, although the degree of certainty should increase as more things become better defined.

Figure 3.6 Project planning

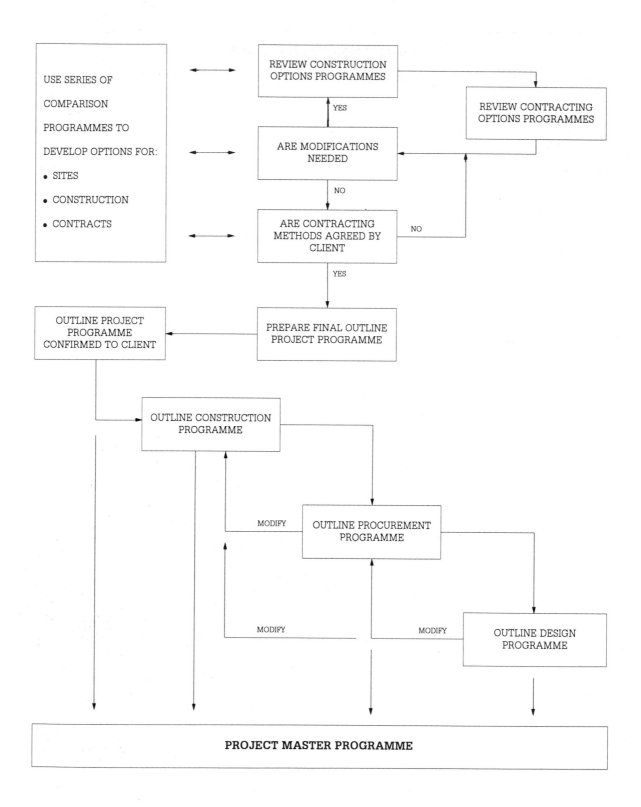

Figure 3.6 (cont)   Project planning

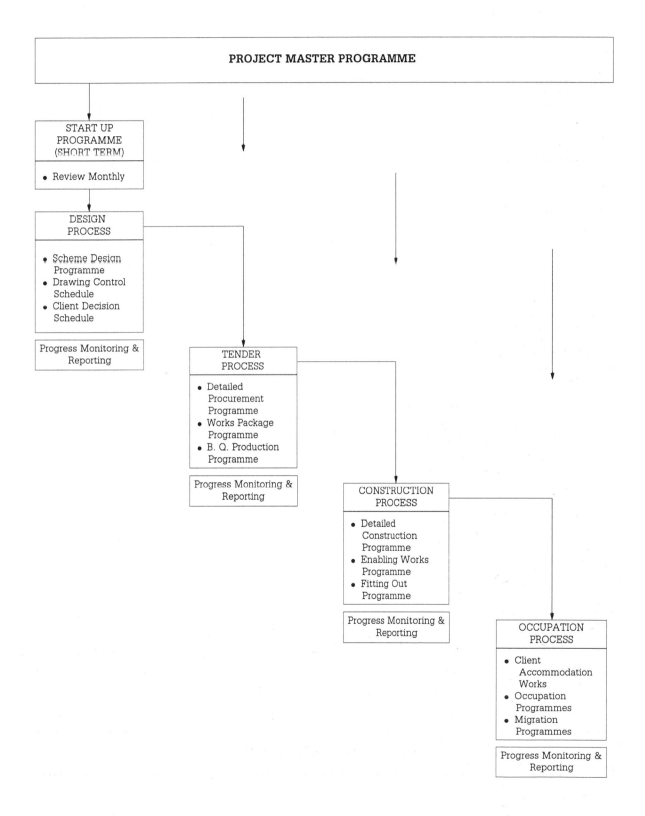

In addition to the design cost plan and contingency, an allowance should be made for professional fees, direct costs and the Client's reserve (this must be determined by the Client). Each section of the cost plan should have its own contingency. The cost plan total is the target within which the project is to be completed.

The cost plan should include a cash flow plan, based upon the Master Programme, allocating expenditure and income to each period of the Client's financial year. The expenditures should be given at a stated base-date level and at out-turn levels based upon a stated forecast of inflation. An example of a financial management document is given at Appendix 3.6 and a cash flow plan at Appendix 3.7.

Operational cost targets should be established for the various categories of running costs associated with the facility. This should accompany the capital cost plan and be included in the brief to the Professional Team. The importance of revenue and grants must also be taken into consideration.

Cost control

When the cost plan is in place it serves as a yardstick for the monitoring and control of costs throughout a project. A cost control checklist is given at Appendix 3.8.

This should be used as an aid in setting up detailed cost control procedures for all stages of a project. An example of a cost and variation control procedure is included at Appendix 3.9.

PENDIX 3.1 START UP PROGRAMME

	TYPICAL 'START UP' PROGRAMME														

OJECT MANAGEMENT LTD'

ENT:

Date 01/07/92   Time Now 23/3/92

Project No.   Programme No.

Revision

NT	DESCRIPTION	PERIOD (WKS)	EARLIEST START	MAR 30	APR 92 6	13	20	27	MAY 92 4	11	18	25	JUN 92 1	8	15	22	29	JUL 92 6	13	20
	LEGAL AGREEMENTS																			
)	Finalise Terms of Agreement	6.0	30/3/92																	
)	Sign Agreement	0.0	8/5/92																	
)	Establish Rights of Light Agreement	8.0	30/3/92																	
)	Establish Party Wall Agreements	8.0	30/3/92																	
	CONSULTANTS ROLES & AGREEMENTS																			
)	Establish Roles & Responsibilities	4.0	30/3/92																	
)	Review Additional Appointment Requirements	4.0	30/3/92																	
)	Finalise Professional Agreements: PM	10.0	30/3/92																	
)	: QS	10.0	30/3/92																	
)	: Architect	10.0	30/3/92																	
)	: Services Eng	10.0	30/3/92																	
)	: Int Designer	10.0	30/3/92																	
	PROJECT STRATEGY																			
5	Confirm Project Strategy	4.0	6/4/92																	
)	Review Capital Budget	2.0	20/4/92																	
)	Prepare Master Development Programme	4.0	6/4/92																	
)	Prepare Cash Flow Forecast	1.0	27/4/92																	
)	Client Approval to Programme & Budget	0.1	4/5/92																	
)	Review Project Procedures Manual	2.0	30/3/92																	
)	Develop Design Programme	4.0	30/3/92																	
	OCCUPANCY BRIEF																			
)	Confirm Extent of Occupation	5.0	30/3/92																	
)	Confirm Location of Occupied Floors	5.0	30/3/92																	
)	Confirm Definition of Occupying Depts	5.0	30/3/92																	
)	Confirm Policy for Tenants Occupation	5.0	30/3/92																	
)	Confirm FO Standard of Building	5.0	30/3/92																	
)	Confirm Target Occupation Date(s)	5.0	30/3/92																	
)	Issue Occupancy Policy Statement	0.1	1/5/92																	
	DEPARTMENTAL SPACE ALLOCATION																			
)	Define Headcount/Growth/Workstation Footprint	4.0	4/5/92																	
)	Define Area of Occupying Depts	4.0	4/5/92																	
)	Define Dept'l Synergy/Adjacency Requirements	4.0	4/5/92																	
)	Establish Policy for Catering Requirement	4.0	1/6/92																	
)	Establish Policy for Security Requirements	4.0	1/6/92																	
)	Establish Policy for General/Archive Storage	4.0	1/6/92																	
)	Establish Policy for Shared Facilities	4.0	1/6/92																	
)	Confirm Support Facilities Required for Occupation	4.0	1/6/92																	
)	Establish Policy for Furniture	9.0	4/5/92																	
)	Establish Leasing Policy for FF & E	9.0	4/5/92																	
)	Determine Finishes Statement	9.0	4/5/92																	
)	Determine Engineering Services Statement	9.0	4/5/92																	
)	Determine IT Statement	9.0	4/5/92																	
	SCHEME DESIGN: ARCHITECTURAL																			
)	Prepare Base Floor Layouts	2.0	30/3/92																	
2	Develop Modular Concept	2.0	30/3/92																	
5	Review Modular Layout on all Floors	4.0	27/4/92																	
)	Appraise Suspended Ceiling Systems	9.0	27/4/92																	
)	Appraise Raised Floor Systems	9.0	27/4/92																	
	SCHEME DESIGN: BUILDING SERVICES																			
)	Appraise Air Conditioning Concepts	9.0	6/4/92																	
)	Appraise Heating Concepts	9.0	6/4/92																	
)	Appraise Ventilation Concepts	9.0	6/4/92																	
)	Appraise Fire Protection Concepts	9.0	6/4/92																	
)	Appraise Fire Detection Concepts	9.0	6/4/92																	
)	Appraise Security Concepts	9.0	6/4/92																	
)	Appraise Plumbing System	9.0	6/4/92																	
)	Appraise Power Distribution Concepts	9.0	6/4/92																	
)	Appraise Building Management Systems	9.0	6/4/92																	
)	Appraise Energy Efficiency Concepts	9.0	6/4/92																	
	SCHEME DESIGN: IT																			
)	Appraise Cabling Concept & Policy	9.0	6/4/92																	
)	Appraise Data Distribution System	9.0	6/4/92																	
)	Appraise Voice System Concept	9.0	6/4/92																	

APPENDIX 3.2 MASTER DEVELOPMENT PROGRAMME

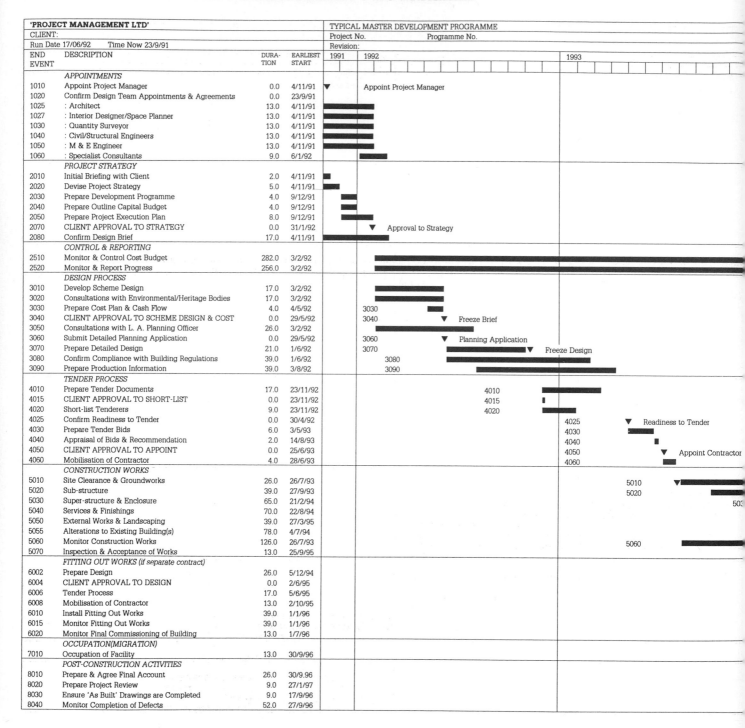

'PROJECT MANAGEMENT LTD'			TYPICAL MASTER DEVELOPMENT PROGRAMME
CLIENT:			Project No. Programme No.
Run Date 17/06/92 Time Now 23/9/91			Revision:

END EVENT	DESCRIPTION	DURA-TION	EARLIEST START
	APPOINTMENTS		
1010	Appoint Project Manager	0.0	4/11/91
1020	Confirm Design Team Appointments & Agreements	0.0	23/9/91
1025	: Architect	13.0	4/11/91
1027	: Interior Designer/Space Planner	13.0	4/11/91
1030	: Quantity Surveyor	13.0	4/11/91
1040	: Civil/Structural Engineers	13.0	4/11/91
1050	: M & E Engineer	13.0	4/11/91
1060	: Specialist Consultants	9.0	6/1/92
	PROJECT STRATEGY		
2010	Initial Briefing with Client	2.0	4/11/91
2020	Devise Project Strategy	5.0	4/11/91
2030	Prepare Development Programme	4.0	9/12/91
2040	Prepare Outline Capital Budget	4.0	9/12/91
2050	Prepare Project Execution Plan	8.0	9/12/91
2070	CLIENT APPROVAL TO STRATEGY	0.0	31/1/92
2080	Confirm Design Brief	17.0	4/11/91
	CONTROL & REPORTING		
2510	Monitor & Control Cost Budget	282.0	3/2/92
2520	Monitor & Report Progress	256.0	3/2/92
	DESIGN PROCESS		
3010	Develop Scheme Design	17.0	3/2/92
3020	Consultations with Environmental/Heritage Bodies	17.0	3/2/92
3030	Prepare Cost Plan & Cash Flow	4.0	4/5/92
3040	CLIENT APPROVAL TO SCHEME DESIGN & COST	0.0	29/5/92
3050	Consultations with L. A. Planning Officer	26.0	3/2/92
3060	Submit Detailed Planning Application	0.0	29/5/92
3070	Prepare Detailed Design	21.0	1/6/92
3080	Confirm Compliance with Building Regulations	39.0	1/6/92
3090	Prepare Production Information	39.0	3/8/92
	TENDER PROCESS		
4010	Prepare Tender Documents	17.0	23/11/92
4015	CLIENT APPROVAL TO SHORT-LIST	0.0	23/11/92
4020	Short-list Tenderers	9.0	23/11/92
4025	Confirm Readiness to Tender	0.0	30/4/92
4030	Prepare Tender Bids	6.0	3/5/93
4040	Appraisal of Bids & Recommendation	2.0	14/8/93
4050	CLIENT APPROVAL TO APPOINT	0.0	25/6/93
4060	Mobilisation of Contractor	4.0	28/6/93
	CONSTRUCTION WORKS		
5010	Site Clearance & Groundworks	26.0	26/7/93
5020	Sub-structure	39.0	27/9/93
5030	Super-structure & Enclosure	65.0	21/2/94
5040	Services & Finishings	70.0	22/8/94
5050	External Works & Landscaping	39.0	27/3/95
5055	Alterations to Existing Building(s)	78.0	4/7/94
5060	Monitor Construction Works	126.0	26/7/93
5070	Inspection & Acceptance of Works	13.0	25/9/95
	FITTING OUT WORKS (if separate contract)		
6002	Prepare Design	26.0	5/12/94
6004	CLIENT APPROVAL TO DESIGN	0.0	2/6/95
6006	Tender Process	17.0	5/6/95
6008	Mobilisation of Contractor	13.0	2/10/95
6010	Install Fitting Out Works	39.0	1/1/96
6015	Monitor Fitting Out Works	39.0	1/1/96
6020	Monitor Final Commissioning of Building	13.0	1/7/96
	OCCUPATION(MIGRATION)		
7010	Occupation of Facility	13.0	30/9/96
	POST-CONSTRUCTION ACTIVITIES		
8010	Prepare & Agree Final Account	26.0	30/9.96
8020	Prepare Project Review	9.0	27/1/97
8030	Ensure 'As Built' Drawings are Completed	9.0	17/9/96
8040	Monitor Completion of Defects	52.0	27/9/96

	1995	1996	1997

Site

5040
5050
5055

5070 ▼ Construction Complete

6002
6004 ▼ Approval to Design
6006
6008
6010
6015
6020

FINAL OCCUPATION

7010

8010
8020
8030
8040

APPENDIX 3.3   OUTLINE DESIGN PROGRAMME

'PROJECT MANAGEMENT LTD'		TYPICAL OUTLINE DESIGN PROGRAMME
CLIENT:		Project No. Programme No.
Run Date 01/07/92 Time Now 30/3/92		Revision:

END EVENT	DESCRIPTION	PERIOD (WKS)	EARLIEST START	AUG 92					SEP 92			
				3	10	17	24	31	7	14	21	28
	DETAIL DESIGN: ARCHITECTURAL											
5020	Suspended Ceilings : 1:20 Sections & Details	12.0	7/9/92				5020					
5030	: Specification	4.0	2/11/92									
5050	Raised Floors : 1:20 Sections & Details	12.0	7/9/92				5050					
5060	: Specification	4.0	2/11/92									
5070	Lobbies & Cores : 1:20 Layouts	10.0	5/10/92								5070	
5080	: 1:20 Sections & Details	10.0	5/10/92								5080	
5090	: Specification	4.0	16/11/92									
5100	Risers : 1:20 Layouts	10.0	5/10/92								5100	
5110	: 1:20 Sections & Details	10.0	5/10/92								5110	
5120	: Specification	4.0	16/11/92									
5125	Non-standard Areas : Details & Specification	5.0	14/12/92									
5130	Carpets : Details & Specification	5.0	14/12/92									
5140	Blinds : Details & Specification	5.0	14/12/92									
5150	Joinery : Details & Specification	5.0	14/12/92									
5160	Wall Finishings : Details & Specification	5.0	14/12/92									
	DETAIL DESIGN: BUILDING SERVICES											
6010	Mechanical Services : 1: 50 Layouts	12.0	7/9/92				6010					
6020	: 1:20 Sections & Details	12.0	21/9/92						6020			
6030	: Specification	6.0	2/11/92									
6040	Lighting & Fire Alarms : 1: 50 Layouts	12.0	21/9/92						6040			
6050	: 1:20 Sections & Details	12.0	5/10/92								6050	
6060	: Specification	6.0	16/11/92									
6070	Power & Telecommunications : 1: 50 Layouts	12.0	21/9/92						6070			
6080	: 1:20 Details/Sections	12.0	5/10/92								6080	
6090	: Specification	6.0	16/11/92									
6100	HVAC Power : 1: 50 Layouts	12.0	5/10/92								6100	
6110	: 1:20 Sections & Details	12.0	19/10/92									
6120	: Specification	6.0	30/11/92									
6130	Public Health Services : 1: 50 Layouts	12.0	19/10/92									
6140	: 1:20 Sections & Details	12.0	2/11/92									
6150	: Specification	6.0	14/12/92									
6160	Sprinkler Services : 1: 50 Layouts	12.0	7/9/92				6160					
6170	: 1:20 Sections & Details	12.0	21/9/92				6170					
6180	: Specification	6.0	2/11/92									
6190	Co-ordinated Layouts : 1: 50	8.0	7/12/92									
6200	Escalators : 1:20 Details	6.0	7/9/92				6200					
6210	: Specification	6.0	7/9/92				6210					
6220	Vehicle Lift : 1:20 Details	6.0	7/9/92				6220					
6230	: Specification	6.0	7/9/92				6230					
6240	Security System : 1:50 Layouts	10.0	21/9/92				6240					
6250	: 1:20 Sections & Details	10.0	5/10/92								6250	
6260	: Specification	6.0	2/11/92									
	DETAIL DESIGN: INFORMATION TECHNOLOGY											
7010	Voice Systems : Comms Room Layouts	6.0	7/9/92				7010					
7020	: Cabling Distribution Layouts	12.0	21/9/92				7020					
7030	: Specification	9.0	2/11/92									
7040	Data Systems : Comms Room Layouts	6.0	7/9/92				7040					
	: Cabling Distribution Layouts	12.0	21/9/92				7050					
	: Specification	9.0	2/11/92									
	DETAIL DESIGN: STRUCTURAL											
8010	Holes Layouts & Details	4.0	5/10/92								8010	
8020	Floor Strengthening Details & Specification	4.0	5/10/92								8020	

				NOV 92					DEC 92				JAN 93				FEB 93	
92	12	19	26	2	9	16	23	30	7	14	21	28	4	11	18	25	1	8

5030
5060
5090
5120
5125
5130
5140
5150
5160
6030
6060
6090
6120
6150
6190

APPENDIX 3.4 PROCUREMENT OPTIONS PROGRAMME

'PROJECT MANAGEMENT LTD'		TYPICAL PROCUREMENT OPTIONS COMPARISON PROGRAMME	
CLIENT:			
Run Date: 30/01/92 Time Now 16/12/91		Project No. Programme No.	

ACT. NO.	DESCRIPTION	DURA-TION	1992
	PRE-PROCUREMENT ACTIVITIES		
10	APPOINT PROJECT MANAGER	0.0	
20	APPOINTMENT OF CONSULTANTS	4.0	
30	DEVELOP PROJECT STRATEGY	4.0	
40	DEVELOP BRIEF	9.0	
50	PREPARE SCHEME DESIGN	17.0	
60	RESOLVE PLANNING ISSUES	17.0	60
70	PREPARE DETAILED DESIGN	39.0	70
	PROCUREMENT OPTION 1: DESIGN & BUILD		
1010	Prepare Tender Documents	4.0	1010
1020	Short-list Tenderers	4.0	1020
1030	Tender Process	10.0	1030
1040	Appointment of D/B Contractor	0.0	1040
1050	Design & Procurement	52.0	1050
1060	Construction Works	91.0	1060
1070	Clients Accommodation Works	26.0	
1080	Occupation	13.0	
	PROCUREMENT OPTION 2: 2 STAGE TENDER		
2010	Prepare 1st Stage Tender Documents	4.0	2010
2020	Short-list Tenderers	4.0	2020
2030	1st Stage Tender Process	6.0	2030
2040	Appointment of Contractor	0.0	2040
2050	Prepare 2nd Stage Tender Documents	21.0	2050
2060	2nd Stage Tender Process	26.0	2060
2070	Agree Final Lump Sum Price	2.0	2070
2080	Construction Works	91.0	2080
2090	Clients Accommodation Works	26.0	
2100	Occupation	13.0	
	PROCUREMENT OPTION 3: CONST. MANAGEMENT/MAN. CONTRACTING		
3010	Prepare Tender Documents	4.0	3010
3020	Short-list Tenderers	4.0	3020
3030	Selection Process	6.0	3030
3040	Appointment of CM/MC	0.0	3040
3050	Prepare Package Tender Documents	39.0	3050
3060	Tender Process for Sub-contract Packages	39.0	3060
3070	Appointment & Mobilisation of Sub-contractors	65.0	3070
3080	Construction Works	91.0	308
3090	Client Accommodation Works	26.0	
3100	Occupation	13.0	
	PROCUREMENT OPTION 4: SINGLE STAGE COMPETITIVE TENDER		
4010	Prepare Tender Documents	21.0	4010
4020	Short-list Tenderers	4.0	402
4030	Tender Process	10.0	
4040	Appointment of Contractor	0.0	
4050	Mobilisation of Contractor	2.0	
4060	Construction Works	91.0	
4070	Clients Accommodation Works	26.0	
4080	Occupation	13.0	

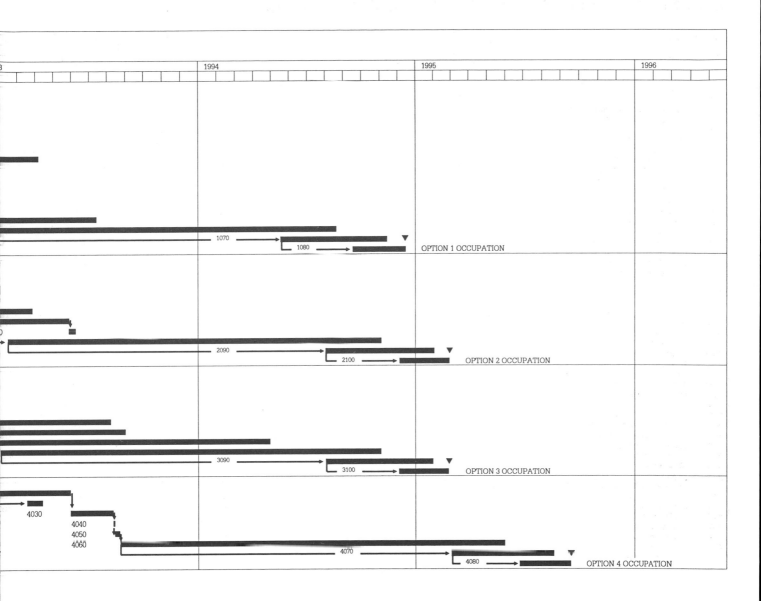

APPENDIX 3.5 OUTLINE CONSTRUCTION PROGRAMME

'PROJECT MANAGEMENT LTD'				TYPICAL OUTLINE CONSTRUCTION PROGRAMME				
CLIENT:				Project No.	Programme No.			
Run Date 17/06/92 Time Now 1/1/91				Revision:				
END EVENT	DESCRIPTION	PERIOD (WKS)	EARLIEST START	EARLIEST FINISH	1991			
					SEP	OCT	NOV	DE
	SUB-STRUCTURE							
5	Piling	13.0	2/9/91	29/11/91	▬▬▬		▬▬▬	
10	Form Pile Caps & Grd Beams	12.0	4/11/91	7/2/92		10	▬▬	
20	U/S Drainage & Form Ground Slab	8.0	2/12/91	7/2/91		20		▬
	FRAME							
30	Form R. C. Frame	16.0	20/1/92	15/5/92			30	
40	Form Concrete Floor Slabs	16.0	3/2/92	29/5/92				
50	Form Stairs	16.0	17/2/92	12/6/92				
	ENCLOSURE & ROOFING							
60	External Brickwork	17.0	30/3/92	31/7/92				
70	Windows	13.0	1/6/92	28/8/92				
80	Form Roof Structure	7.0	1/6/92	17/7/92				
90	Roof Finishings	4.0	17/8/92	11/9/92				
100	Window Cleaning Equipment	5.0	14/9/92	16/10/92				
	SERVICES & FINISHINGS							
110	Install Services to Risers	17.0	18/5/92	11/9/92				
120	Install High Level M & E Services – 1st Fix	17.0	18/5/92	11/9/92				
130	Install Suspended Ceilings	15.0	6/7/92	16/10/92				
140	Install High Level M & E Services – 2nd Fix	13.0	3/8/92	30/10/92				
150	Blockwork	13.0	30/3/92	3/7/92				
160	Install Raised Floors	15.0	17/8/92	27/11/92				
170	Plant Room Installations	24.0	3/8/92	29/1/93				
180	Install Lifts	18.0	14/9/92	29/1/93				
190	Toilet Installations	26.0	17/8/92	26/2/93				
200	Entrance Screens	4.0	31/8/92	25/9/92				
210	Plaster Works	13.0	1/6/92	28/8/92				
220	Joinery	18.0	31/8/92	15/1/93				
230	Painting & Decorations	8.0	18/1/93	12/3/93				
240	Carpets	8.0	1/3/93	30/4/93				
250	Commission Services	17.0	14/12/92	30/4/93				
260	Final Snag & Clean	4.0	29/3/93	30/4/93				
	EXTERNAL WORKS							
270	External Works	22.0	19/10/92	2/4/93				
280	External Landscaping	13.0	4/1/93	2/4/93				

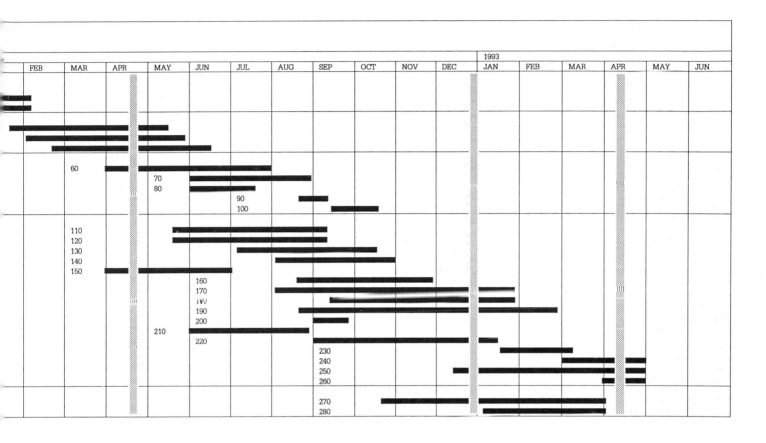

	FEB	MAR	APR	MAY	JUN	JUL	AUG	SEP	OCT	NOV	DEC	1993 JAN	FEB	MAR	APR	MAY	JUN

APPENDIX 3.6 FINANCIAL MANAGEMENT DOCUMENT

Project Management Ltd

PROJECT: 'XYZ REDEVELOPMENT SCHEME'
         (SHELL & CORE)
         Project No:

CLIENT: 'A.B.C. Construction Management Limited'

Date: 6th February 1992
(Period up to end of January 1992)

Index

PROJECT DATA SHEET

'XYZ Redevelopment Scheme' (Shell and Core)	Feb-92

GENERAL PROJECT INFORMATION

GROSS EXTERNAL FLOOR AREA:	41,341 sq m (444,530 sq ft)
NET LETTABLE FLOOR AREA:	29,230 sq m (314,300 sq ft)
TYPE OF CONTRACT:	JCT '80 (With Quants) Two Stage

CONSTRUCTION PROGRAMME INFORMATION

PROGRAMME REF:	GS/MDP/3 Rev C (28-Nov-90)
COMMENCEMENT DATE:	03-Dec-90
CONTRACT PERIOD:	29 Months
COMPLETION DATE:	26-Apr-93
EXTENSION OF TIME GRANTED:	None
REVISED COMPLETION DATE:	N/A
CURRENT PROGRAMME STATUS:	See elsewhere

FINANCIAL INFORMATION

CURRENT BUDGET:		
VFM 3 (Shell & Core):	103,983,000.00	(Nov-90)
VFM 3 (Early Start Works (90/91)):	920,000.00	(Nov-90)
ENHANCEMENTS:	20,000.00	E1 only
TOTAL OF SANCTIONS	£104,923,000.00	
CHANGE ORDERS INCLUDED:	D1–D28 & E1	
QS BUDGET INCORPORATED:	Report No 7	(04-Feb-92)

CASH FLOW SUMMARY

YEAR	AGREED CASHFLOW (31-12-91)	CURRENT CASHFLOW (06-02-92)	VARIANCE (Agreed to Current)
	£	£	£
Up to 1989	2,653,420.32	2,651,420.32	0.00
1990	3,296,431.44	3,296,431.44	0.00
1991	12,021,429.41	12,021,429.41	0.00
1992	52,966,485.19	52,908,877.53	(57,607.66)
1993	10,095,472.15	10,072,390.96	(23,081.19)
1994	3,628,882.74	3,611,938.57	(16,944.17)
1995	133,313.44	127,626.75	(5,686.69)
Non cashflowed	20,127,565.31	20,230,885.02	103,319.71
TOTAL	104,923,000.00	104,923,000.00	0.00

BUDGET SUMMARY

	APPROVED SANCTION	CAPITAL BUDGET (27-06-91)	CURRENT COST PLAN (06-02-92)	PREVIOUS FORECAST (31-12-91)	CURRENT FORECAST (06-02-92)	VARIANCE (Cost Plan to Forecast)
	£	£	£	£	£	£
1.00 Development Costs	3,870,000.00	1,056,688.89	745,191.89	745,191.89	745,191.89	0.00
2.00 Construction Costs	78,295,999.00	81,376,500.00	73,769,414.93	73,769,414.93	73,769,414.93	0.00
3.00 Professional Fees & Expenses	11,217,163.00	11,576,876.39	11,600,452.56	11,600,452.56	11,600,452.56	0.00
4.00 Other Related Costs	2,625,837.00	1,755,230.77	1,790,803.27	1,790,803.27	1,790,803.27	0.00
5.00 Early Start Works (1990/91)	920,000.00	150,000.00	90,406.59	90,406.59	90,406.59	0.00
6.00 Client (Fee) Contingency	2,705,000.00	707,057.00	692,875.93	692,875.93	692,875.93	0.00
7.00 VAT	2,475,000.00	170,000.00	170,000.00	170,000.00	170,000.00	0.00
Sub-total	102,108,999.00	96,792,353.05	88,859,145.17	88,859,145.17	88,859,145.17	0.00
8.00 Development Reserve	2,795,000.00	8,130,646.95	16,063,854.83	16,063,854.83	16,063,854.83	0.00
TOTAL	£104,903,000.00	£104,923,999.00	£104,923,000.00	£104,923,000.00	£104,923,000.00	£0.00

NOTES ON USE OF THIS DATA SHEET

Approved Sanction Column shows the sums included in the VFM3s.

Capital Budget column shows the values that were generated when the VFM3s were dissected into more detailed cost centres. The Capital Budget has been approved by ABCCML

The Current Cost Plan column in Capital Budget values adjusted for approved Change Orders. This column therefore sets the cost targets against which the Current Forecast is compared.

The Current Forecast is the latest estimate of the final cost.

The Variance column shows the difference between the estimated final cost (Current Forecast) and the authorised cost limit (Current Cost Plan). Variances identify areas where action is required, be it savings or funding.

NOTES & BRIEF INTERPRETATION ON FINANCIAL DATA

1. This Report includes the adjustments required by ABCCM (letter 31/12/91) and the Authorised to Date values concur with ABCCM's records for the period up to and including December 1991.

2. The substantial variance in the monthly cash flow for February 1992 and April 1992 (Sheet 7) is primarily due to a revised cashflow.

3. The 'Authorised to date' figures are values authorised up to and including the end of January 1992.

4. The Shell & Core Cash flow values (Sheets 5 and 6) relate to the Current Forecast values above. To ensure that the currently unfunded items are cashflowed correctly, the Development Reserve has been adjusted.

Action by

APPENDIX 3.6 FINANCIAL MANAGEMENT DOCUMENT Sheet 3

PROJECT FINANCIAL SUMMARY

Cost Group	Title	Capital Budget (27-06-91) £	Current Cost Plan £	Previous Forecast £	Current Forecast £	Variance (Cost Plan to Forecast) £	Authorised to Date £
1.00	Development Costs	1,056,688.89	745,191.89	745,191.89	745,191.89	0.00	452,021.79
2.00	Construction Costs	81,376,500.00	73,769,414.93	73,769,414.93	73,769,414.93	0.00	10,722,011.11
3.00	Professional Fees & Expenses	11,576,876.39	11,600,452.56	11,600,452.56	11,600,452.56	0.00	7,002,420.14
4.00	Other Related Costs	1,755,230.77	1,790,803.27	1,790,803.27	1,790,803.27	0.00	1,503,007.60
5.00	Early Start Works (1990/91)	150,000.00	90,406.59	90,406.59	90,406.59	0.00	83,906.59
6.00	Client (Fee) Contingency	707,057.00	692,875.93	692,875.93	692,875.93	0.00	0.00
7.00	VAT	170,000.00	170,000.00	170,000.00	170,000.00	0.00	90,383.29
	Sub-Total	96,792,353.05	88,859,145.17	88,859,145.17	88,859,145.17	0.00	19,853,750.52
8.00	Development Reserve	8,130,646.95	16,063,854.83	16,063,854.83	16,063,854.83	0.00	0.00
	Total	104,923,000.00	104,923,000.00	104,923,000.00	104,923,000.00	0.00	19,853,750.52

Cost Code	Element	Capital Budget (27-06-91) £	Current Cost Plan £	Previous Forecast £	Current Forecast £	Variance (Cost Plan to Forecast) £	Authorised to Date £	Remarks
	Cost Group 1.00 – Development Costs							
1.60	Acceleration Exercise (1989) Neighbouring Properties	28,702.95	28,702.95	28,702.95	28,702.95	0.00	28,702.95	Cost Centre Closed
1.71	Rights of Light – Compensation	632,000.00	140,000.00	140,000.00	140,000.00	0.00	40,000.00	
1.72	Rights of Light – Other Parties Fees (Technical & Legal)	22,000.00	30,000.00	30,000.00	30,000.00	0.00	10,672.13	
1.73	Tower Crane Oversail – Compensation	81,000.00	111,500.00	111,500.00	111,500.00	0.00	87,700.00	
1.74	Tower Crane Oversail – Other Parties Fees (Technical & Legal)	20,000.00	35,000.00	35,000.00	35,000.00	0.00	26,993.66	
1.75	Monitoring of G. & T. Consultants	17,250.00	40,000.00	40,000.00	40,000.00	0.00	17,555.70	
1.76	Schedules of Conditions – Other Parties Fees	36,000.00	36,000.00	36,000.00	36,000.00	0.00	6,610.00	
1.77	SB Fees	94,735.94	94,735.94	94,735.94	94,735.94	0.00	66,059.97	
1.78	ABCCM Legal Fees	90,000.00	150,000.00	150,000.00	150,000.00	0.00	121,969.28	
1.79	Nuisance/Disturbance – Compensation	0.00	50,000.00	50,000.00	50,000.00	0.00	16,505.10	
1.90	Archaeological Investigations	35,000.00	29,253.00	29,253.00	29,253.00	0.00	29,253.00	Cost Centre Closed
	Total	1,056,688.89	745,191.89	745,191.89	745,191.89	0.00	452,021.79	
	Cost Group 2.00 – Construction Costs							
2.10	Ground Investigation & Enabling Works	376,500.00	289,414.93	289,414.93	289,414.93	0.00	214,428.48	
2.15	Hoarding Artwork	0.00	100,000.00	100,000.00	100,000.00	0.00	77,582.63	
2.30	Direct Orders Attributable to Construction Costs	0.00	0.00	0.00	0.00	0.00	0.00	
2.50	Main Construction Contract	69,836,853.06	68,322,803.06	68,344,803.06	68,322,803.06	0.00	10,430,000.00	See G & T Report No 6 (amended to include latest Change Orders). Cost Plan includes Change Order C7, C9–C11, C16–C23, D17, D21 & C24–C33
2.90	Construction Contingency	11,163,146.94	5,057,196.94	5,035,196.94	5,057,196.94	0.00	0.00	
	Total	81,376,500.00	73,769,414.93	73,769,414.93	73,769,414.93	0.00	10,722,011.11	
	Cost Group 3.00 – Professional Fees & Expenses							
3.01	Project Manager	1,226,113.37	1,246,113.37	1,246,113.37	1,246,113.37	0.00	784,763.72	Project Management Ltd
3.02	Architect	4,515,874.61	4,485,874.61	4,485,874.61	4,485,874.61	0.00	2,053,515.74	G.A. Partnership
3.03	Quantity Surveyor	1,646,189.05	1,646,189.05	1,646,189.05	1,646,189.05	0.00	773,510.15	G. & T.
3.04	Building Services Consultant	1,538,574.79	1,538,574.79	1,538,574.79	1,538,574.79	0.00	1,412,557.36	F. Partnership
3.05	Structural Engineer	963,851.46	963,851.46	963,851.46	963,851.46	0.00	813,053.62	O. & D. Consulting Engineers
3.14	Building Surveys	90,000.00	80,542.60	80,542.60	80,542.60	0.00	80,542.60	G. & S. & T. & Partners
3.20	On Site Quality Managers	233,000.00	233,000.00	233,000.00	233,000.00	0.00	22,513.00	Various
3.24	Construction Advisor	240,000.00	240,000.00	240,000.00	240,000.00	0.00	240,000.00	S L International
3.26	Independent Testing & Inspections	260,000.00	260,000.00	260,000.00	260,000.00	0.00	17,486.31	S. B. Consultants
3.27	Design Monitoring	53,150.00	53,150.00	53,150.00	53,150.00	0.00	14,696.32	J. Bloggs Esq
3.28	Archaeological Consultant	4,500.00	3,352.50	3,352.50	3,352.50	0.00	3,352.50	B&B Ltd
3.29	Site Photography	10,000.00	10,000.00	10,000.00	10,000.00	0.00	4,817.00	Foto Fix
3.30	Asbestos Survey	14,980.00	14,980.00	14,980.00	14,980.00	0.00	14,980.00	A A. Analysis Ltd
	Carried Forward	10,796,233.28	10,775,628.38	10,775,628.38	10,775,628.38	0.00	6,235,788.32	

PROJECT FINANCIAL SUMMARY continued

Cost Code	Element	Capital Budget (27-06-91) £	Current Cost Plan £	Previous Forecast £	Current Forecast £	Variance (Cost Plan to Forecast) £	Authorised to Date £	Remarks
	Brought Forward	10,796,233.28	10,775,628.38	10,775,628.38	10,775,628.38	0.00	6,235,788.32	
3.51	Additional Services	1,728.19	1,728.19	1,728.19	1,728.19	0.00	1,728.19	Project Management Ltd
3.52	Additional Services	454,516.04	468,697.11	468,697.11	468,697.11	0.00	468,697.11	G.A. Partnership
3.53	Additional Services	34,000.00	34,000.00	34,000.00	34,000.00	0.00	34,000.00	G. & T.
3.54	Additional Services	86,679.80	86,679.80	86,679.80	86,679.80	0.00	57,473.72	F. P. Partnership
3.55	Additional Services	44,500.00	44,500.00	44,500.00	44,500.00	0.00	34,863.49	O. & C. Consulting Engineers
3.56	Conceptual M & E Design	74,872.46	74,872.46	74,872.46	74,872.46	0.00	74,872.46	J.B. & C. Partners
3.57	Pre-Contract Services	52,190.44	52,190.44	52,190.44	52,190.44	0.00	52,190.44	O.A.B. & Partners
3.58	Reimbursement for Overseas Travel	0.00	30,000.00	30,000.00	30,000.00	0.00	10,650.23	
3.80	Sundry Fees	32,156.18	32,156.18	32,156.18	32,156.18	0.00	32,156.18	
	Carried Forward	11,576,876.39	11,600,452.56	11,600,452.56	11,600,452.56	0.00	7,002,420.14	
	Cost Group 4.00 – Other Related Costs							
4.01	Building Regulations	403,140.00	403,140.00	403,140.00	403,140.00	0.00	201,570.00	
4.02	Planning Fees	5,058.48	5,058.48	5,058.48	5,058.48	0.00	5,058.48	
4.03	Credit Checks	5,000.00	5,000.00	5,000.00	5,000.00	0.00	315.00	
4.04	Project Insurances	150,000.00	170,343.75	170,343.75	170,343.75	0.00	147,662.24	
4.40	Miscellaneous Expenditure	34,769.91	50,000.00	50,000.00	50,000.00	0.00	35,213.61	
4.60	ABCCML Unallocated Costs	16,104.49	16,103.15	16,103.15	16,103.15	0.00	16,103.15	Cost Centre Closed
4.70	ABCCML Design & Management Fee	1,020,000.00	1,020,000.00	1,020,000.00	1,020,000.00	0.00	1,020,000.00	Cost Centre Closed
4.80	ABCCML Direct & Legal Costs	121,157.89	121,157.89	121,157.89	121,157.89	0.00	77,085.12	
	Total	1,755,230.77	1,790,803.27	1,790,803.27	1,790,803.27	0.00	1,503,007.60	
	Cost Group 5.00 – Early Start Works (1990/91)							
5.01	Project Manager	40,000.00	32,923.00	32,923.00	32,923.00	0.00	32,923.00	Project Management Ltd
5.02	Architect	12,500.00	4,560.12	4,560.12	4,560.12	0.00	4,560.12	G.A. Partnership
5.03	Quantity Surveyor	12,500.00	12,500.00	12,500.00	12,500.00	0.00	6,000.00	G. & T.
5.04	Building Services Consultant	10,000.00	900.00	900.00	900.00	0.00	900.00	F.P. Partnership
5.05	Structural Engineer	40,000.00	39,523.47	39,523.47	39,523.47	0.00	39,523.47	O. & C. Consulting Engineers
5.50	Constr. Contract (included in cost centre 2.50)	0.00	0.00	0.00	0.00	0.00	0.00	Gen. Construction Ltd
5.80	Fee Contingency	35,000.00	0.00	0.00	0.00	0.00	0.00	
	Total	150,000.00	90,406.59	90,406.59	90,406.59	0.00	83,906.59	
	Cost Group 6.00 – Client (Fee) Contingency							
	Fee Contingency	707,057.00	692,875.93	692,875.93	692,875.93	0.00	0.00	
	Total	707,057.00	692,875.93	692,875.93	692,875.93	0.00	0.00	
	Cost Group 7.00 – VAT							
	Unrecoverable VAT (to Dec '89)	90,383.29	90,383.29	90,383.29	90,383.29	0.00	90,383.29	As advised by P. Black Esq.
	Allowance for further items of unrecoverable VAT	79,616.71	79,616.71	79,616.71	79,616.71	0.00	0.00	As advised by P. Black Esq. Further VAT liability to be assessed.
	Total	170,000.00	170,000.00	170,000.00	170,000.00	0.00	90,383.29	
	Cost Group 8.00 – Development Reserve							
8.10	*General Reserve*							
8.11	Funds retrieved from Early Start Works	420,000.00	479,593.41	479,593.41	479,593.41	0.00	N/A	£75,000 funded from Constr. Contg
8.12	FHCML direct and legal cost surplus	290,849.95	290,849.95	290,849.95	290,849.95	0.00	N/A	
8.13	FHCML general reserve	7,419,797.00	7,673,411.47	7,673,411.47	7,673,411.47	0.00	N/A	
8.14	Transfers to fit-out	0.00	120,000.00	120,000.00	120,000.00	0.00	N/A	Reception desks (Change Order D21)
8.20	*Construction Reserve*							
8.21	Construction Reserve	0.00	7,500,000.00	7,500,000.00	7,500,000.00	0.00	N/A	
	Total	8,130,646.95	16,063,854.83	16,063,854.83	16,063,854.83	0.00	0.00	

CASH FLOW AS AT 31/12/91

Date	Month No	1 Development Costs	2 Construction Costs	3 Professional Fees	4 Other Related Costs	5 Early Start Works
Up to 12/88		34,314.84	0.00	626,019.71	16,138.23	0.00
1989	1–6	43,081.84	6,919.00	768,942.88	1,050,946.20	0.00
1990	7–18	24,002.47	234,007.41	2,757,580.15	242,574.15	0.00
Jan 91	19	600.00	0.00	256,692.30	0.00	0.00
Feb 91	20	4,334.00	160,000.00	90,261.00	9,000.85	0.00
Mar 91	21	2,200.00	344,000.00	325,256.54	0.00	7,737.68
Apr 91	22	31,355.70	160,000.00	36,697.39	0.00	11,178.83
May 91	23	116,743.84	310,000.00	1,397,373.72	0.00	12,709.44
Jun 91	24	39,847.75	320,000.00	156,549.85	134,934.92	0.00
Jul 91	25	48,509.27	580,905.60	68,865.30	20,092.66	0.00
Aug 91	26	19,647.13	697,373.31	104,535.18	0.00	0.00
Sep 91	27	11,095.15	1,244,552.25	63,737.37	275.00	0.00
Oct 91	28	22,305.36	1,148,316.91	65,747.51	6,108.78	0.00
Nov 91	29	11,482.00	1,550,000.00	140,201.28	22,896.81	52,280.64
Dec 91	30	6,383.69	1,870,675.36	88,861.32	40.00	0.00
Jan 92	31	36,118.75	2,145,261.27	55,098.64	0.00	0.00
Feb 92	32	16,053.00	2,395,000.00	190,467.44	6,260.00	0.00
Mar 92	33	23,553.34	3,171,000.00	87,640.52	6,260.00	6,500.00
Apr 92	34	18,100.00	4,371,000.00	98,856.71	3,230.00	0.00
May 92	35	1,100.00	4,597,000.00	158,046.79	14,330.00	0.00
Jun 92	36	22,900.00	4,512.000.00	1,410,700.73	2,230.00	0.00
Jul 92	37	1,100.00	4,618,000.00	115,616.32	2,230.00	0.00
Aug 92	38	1,100.00	5,197,000.00	160,546.79	2,230.00	0.00
Sep 92	39	1,100.00	5,094,000.00	68,197.93	2,230.00	0.00
Oct 92	40	11,100.00	5,274,000.00	89,156.73	2,230.00	0.00
Nov 92	41	1,100.00	5,042,000.00	148,346.79	103,015.00	0.00
Dec 92	42	6,100.00	3,473,000.00	58,997.93	2,230.00	0.00
Jan 93	43	1,100.00	2,312,000.00	86,597.48	1,220.00	0.00
Feb 93	44	1,100.00	1,798,000.00	149,955.46	1,220.00	0.00
Mar 93	45	1,100.00	1,161,000.00	47,859.57	1,220.00	0.00
Apr 93	46	0.00	795,000.00	28,634.36	1,220.00	0.00
May 93	47	0.00	2,113,803.00	117,481.89	12,601.51	0.00
Jun 93	48	13,030.72	313,000.00	496,252.26	101,805.00	0.00
Jul 93	49	10,000.00	242,000.00	25,339.36	1,020.00	0.00
Aug 93	50	0.00	242,000.00	91,501.17	1,020.00	0.00
Sep 93	51	0.00	162,000.00	3,309.36	1,020.00	0.00
Oct 93	52	0.00	162,000.00	3,309.36	1,020.00	0.00
Nov 93	53	0.00	91,000.00	84,750.35	1,020.00	0.00
Dec 93	54	0.00	0.00	3,309.36	462.77	0.00
Jan 94	55	0.00	0.00	0.00	0.00	0.00
Feb 94	56	0.00	0.00	83,972.60	0.00	0.00
Mar 94	57	0.00	0.00	0.00	0.00	0.00
Apr 94	58	0.00	0.00	0.00	0.00	0.00
May 94	59	0.00	3,025,000.00	93,869.41	0.00	0.00
Jun 94	60	0.00	0.00	409,756.68	0.00	0.00
Jul 94	61	0.00	0.00	0.00	0.00	0.00
Aug 94	62	0.00	0.00	0.00	0.00	0.00
Sep 94	63	0.00	0.00	0.00	0.00	0.00
Oct 94	64	0.00	0.00	0.00	0.00	0.00
Nov 94	65	0.00	0.00	0.00	0.00	0.00
Dec 94	66	0.00	0.00	0.00	0.00	0.00
Jan 95	67	0.00	0.00	0.00	0.00	0.00
Feb 95	68	0.00	0.00	0.00	0.00	0.00
Mar 95	69	0.00	0.00	0.00	0.00	0.00
Apr 95	70	0.00	0.00	0.00	0.00	0.00
May 95	71	0.00	0.00	0.00	0.00	0.00
Jun 95	72	0.00	0.00	127,626.75	0.00	0.00
Jul 95	73	0.00	0.00	0.00	0.00	0.00
Total cashflowed		581,658.85	70,712,814.11	11,442,520.26	1,774,331.88	90,406.59
Uncashflowed funds		163,533.04	3,016,600.82	157,932.30	16,471.39	0.00
Totals		745,191.89	73,729,414.93	11,600.452.56	1,790,803.27	90,406.59

NOTES

Professional fees include allowances for inflation based upon actual RPI indicies for inflation calculations to end of 1991 and 6% thereafter. The cash flow has been based upon the month that the payment will be made.

CASH FLOW AS AT 31/12/91 (CONTINUED)

6 Client (Fee) Contingency	7 VAT Expenditure	7 VAT Recovery	7 VAT Unrecovered	Annual Totals	8 Development Reserve
0.00	90,237.37	(90,237.37)	84,809.65	761,282.43	
0.00	126,374.26	(109,699.93)	5,573.64	1,892,137.89	
0.00	488,538.22	(450,270.96)	0.00	3,296,431.44	
0.00	38,593.85	(54,941.59)	0.00		
0.00	38,849.38	(38,593.85)	0.00		
0.00	101,729.13	(38,849.38)	0.00		
0.00	29,884.79	(101,729.13)	0.00		
0.00	302,650.20	(29,884.79)	0.00		
0.00	83,920.88	(302,650.20)	0.00		
0.00	122,762.16	(83,920.88)	0.00		
0.00	142,963.10	(122,762.16)	0.00		
0.00	230,115.26	(142,963.10)	0.00		
0.00	222,284.81	(230,115.26)	0.00		
0.00	310,399.32	(222,284.81)	0.00		
0.00	344,009.31	(310,399.32)	0.00	12,021,429.41	
0.00	382,219.75	(344,009.31)	0.00		
0.00	438,886.43	(382,219.75)	0.00		
0.00	575,035.57	(438,886.43)	0.00		
0.00	784,289.93	(575,035.57)	0.00		
0.00	817,135.69	(784,289.93)	0.00		
0.00	1,040,725.14	(817,135.69)	0.00		
0.00	831,672.85	(1,040,725.14)	0.00		
0.00	922,398.19	(831,672.85)	0.00		
0.00	903,962.14	(922,398.19)	0.00		
0.00	940,092.43	(903,962.14)	0.00		
0.00	935,275.57	(940,092.43)	0.00		
0.00	619,552.14	(935,275.57)	0.00	52,908,877.53	
0.00	419,367.81	(619,552.14)	0.00		
0.00	339,542.96	(419,367.81)	0.00		
0.00	211,951.18	(339,542.96)	0.00		
0.00	143,556.77	(211,951.18)	0.00		
0.00	390,648.11	(143,556.77)	0.00		
0.00	165,210.16	(390,648.11)	0.00		
0.00	47,920.14	(165,210.16)	0.00		
0.00	58,541.20	(47,920.14)	0.00		
0.00	29,107.64	(58,541.20)	0.00		
0.00	29,107.64	(29,107.64)	0.00		
0.00	30,934.81	(29,107.64)	0.00		
0.00	660.12	(30,934.81)	0.00	10,072,390.96	
0.00	0.00	(660.12)	0.00		
0.00	14,695.21	0.00	0.00		
0.00	0.00	(14,695.21)	0.00		
0.00	0.00	0.00	0.00		
0.00	545,802.15	0.00	0.00		
0.00	71,707.42	(545,802.15)	0.00		
0.00	0.00	(71,707.42)	0.00		
0.00	0.00	0.00	0.00		
0.00	0.00	0.00	0.00		
0.00	0.00	0.00	0.00		
0.00	0.00	0.00	0.00		
0.00	0.00	0.00	0.00	3,611,938.57	
0.00	0.00	0.00	0.00		
0.00	0.00	0.00	0.00		
0.00	0.00	0.00	0.00		
0.00	0.00	0.00	0.00		
0.00	0.00	0.00	0.00		
0.00	22,334.68	0.00	0.00		
0.00	0.00	(22,334.68)	0.00	127,626.75	
0.00	14,385,645.87	(14,385,645.87)	90,383.29	84,692,114.98	
692,875.93	3,567,373.45	(3,567,373.45)	79,616.71	4,167,030.19	16,063,854.83
692,875.93	17,953,019.32	(17,953,019.32)	170,000.00	88,859,145.17	16,063,854.83

	Total of Current Forecast	104,923,004.00

SUMMARY CASH FLOW AS AT 31/01/92

Date	Month No	Agreed Forecast - 31 December '91			Current Forecast			Agreed v Current Deviation	
		Forecast	Annual Cumulative	Total Cumulative	Actual or Forecast	Annual Cumulative	Total Cumulative	Monthly Variation	Annual Cumulative
Up to 1988		761,282.43	761,282.43	761,282.43	761,282.43	761,282.43	761,282.43	0.00	0.00
1989		1,892,137.89	1,892,137.89	2,653,420.32	1,892,137.89	1,892,137.89	2,653,420.32	0.00	0.00
Jan 90	7	251,372.27	251,372.27	2,904,792.59	251,372.27	251,372.27	2,904,792.59	0.00	0.00
Feb 90	8	184,619.44	435,991.71	3,089,412.03	184,619.44	435,991.71	3,089,412.03	0.00	0.00
Mar 90	9	341,737.46	777,729.17	3,431,149.49	341,737.46	777,729.17	3,431,149.49	0.00	0.00
Apr 90	10	154,618.12	932,347.29	3,585,767.61	154,618.12	932,347.29	3,585,767.61	0.00	0.00
May 90	11	53,805.17	986,152.46	3,639,572.78	53,805.17	986,152.46	3,639,572.78	0.00	0.00
Jun 90	12	1,270,810.02	2,256,962.48	4,910,382.80	1,270,810.02	2,256,962.48	4,910,382.80	0.00	0.00
Jul 90	13	(90,812.29)	2,166,150.19	4,819,570.51	(90,812.29)	2,166,150.19	4,819,570.51	0.00	0.00
Aug 90	14	158,886.34	2,325,036.53	4,978,456.85	158,886.34	2,325,036.53	4,978,456.85	0.00	0.00
Sep 90	15	107,978.85	2,433,015.38	5,086,435.70	107,978.85	2,433,015.38	5,086,435.70	0.00	0.00
Oct 90	16	208,068.49	2,641,083.87	5,294,504.19	208,068.49	2,641,083.87	5,294,504.19	0.00	0.00
Nov 90	17	273,650.69	2,914,734.56	5,568,154.88	273,650.69	2,914,734.56	5,568,154.88	0.00	0.00
Dec 90	18	381,696.88	3,296,431.44	5,949,851.76	381,696.88	3,296,431.44	5,949,851.76	0.00	0.00
Jan 91	19	240,944.56	240,944.56	6,190,796.32	240,944.56	240,944.56	6,190,796.32	0.00	0.00
Feb 91	20	263,851.38	504,795.94	6,454,647.70	263,851.38	504,795.94	6,454,647.70	0.00	0.00
Mar 91	21	742,073.97	1,246,869.91	7,196,721.67	742,073.97	1,246,869.91	7,196,721.67	0.00	0.00
Apr 91	22	127,387.58	1,374,257.49	7,324,109.25	127,387.58	1,374,257.49	7,324,109.25	0.00	0.00
May 91	23	2,109,592.41	3,483,849.90	9,433,701.66	2,109,592.41	3,483,849.90	9,433,701.66	0.00	0.00
Jun 91	24	432,603.20	3,916,453.10	9,866,304.86	432,603.20	3,916,453.10	9,866,304.86	0.00	0.00
Jul 91	25	757,214.11	4,673,667.21	10,623,518.97	757,214.11	4,673,667.21	10,623,518.97	0.00	0.00
Aug 91	26	841,756.56	5,515,423.77	11,465,275.53	841,756.56	5,515,423.77	11,465,275.53	0.00	0.00
Sep 91	27	1,406,811.93	6,922,235.70	12,872,087.46	1,406,811.93	6,922,235.70	12,872,087.46	0.00	0.00
Oct 91	28	1,234,648.11	8,156,883.81	14,106,735.57	1,234,648.11	8,156,883.81	14,106,735.57	0.00	0.00
Nov 91	29	1,864,975.24	10,021,859.05	15,971,710.81	1,864,975.24	10,021,859.05	15,971,710.81	0.00	0.00
Dec 91	30	1,999,570.36	12,021,429.41	17,971,281.17	1,999,570.36	12,021,429.41	17,971,281.17	0.00	0.00
Jan 92	31	2,337,966.64	2,337,966.64	20,309,247.81	2,264,689.10	2,264,689.10	20,235,970.27	(73,277.54)	(73,277.54)
Feb 92	32	3,113,523.73	5,451,490.37	23,422,771.54	2,574,447.12	4,839,136.22	22,810,417.39	(539,076.61)	(612,354.15)
Mar 92	33	3,534,641.66	8,986,132.03	26,957,413.20	3,431,103.00	8,270,239.22	26,241,520.39	(103,538.66)	(715,892.81)
Apr 92	34	4,086,442.88	13,072,574.91	31,043,856.08	4,700,441.09	12,970,680.31	30,941,961.48	613,998.21	(101,894.60)
May 92	35	4,685,164.30	17,757,739.21	35,729,020.38	4,713,322.55	17,684,002.86	35,655,284.03	28,158.25	(73,736.35)
Jun 92	36	6,232,006.33	23,989,745.54	41,961,026.71	6,191,420.18	23,875,423.04	41,846,704.21	(40,586.15)	(114,322.50)
Jul 92	37	4,337,364.02	28,327,109.56	46,298,390.73	4,547,894.03	28,423,317.07	46,394,598.24	210,530.01	96,207.51
Aug 92	38	5,394,411.90	33,721,521.46	51,692,802.63	5,361,602.13	33,784,919.20	51,756,200.37	(32,809.77)	63,397.74
Sep 92	39	5,147,268.61	38,868,790.07	56,840,071.24	5,147,091.88	38,932,011.08	56,903,292.25	(176.73)	63,221.01
Oct 92	40	5,552,077.21	44,420,867.28	62,392,148.45	5,412,617.02	44,344,628.10	62,315,909.27	(139,460.19)	(76,239.18)
Nov 92	41	5,320,836.68	49,741,703.96	67,712,985.13	5,339,644.93	49,684,273.03	67,655,554.20	18,808.25	(57,430.93)
Dec 92	42	3,224,781.23	52,966,485.19	70,937,766.36	3,224,604.50	52,908,877.53	70,880,158.70	(176.73)	(57,607.66)
Jan 93	43	2,201,614.23	2,201,614.23	73,139,380.59	2,200,733.15	2,200,733.15	73,080,891.85	(881.08)	(881.08)
Feb 93	44	1,863,761.45	4,065,375.68	75,003,142.04	1,860,450.61	4,061,183.76	74,941,342.46	(3,310.84)	(4,191.92)
Mar 93	45	1,083,897.10	5,149,272.78	76,087,039.14	1,083,587.79	5,144,771.55	76,024,930.25	(309.31)	(4,501.23)
Apr 93	46	756,432.80	5,905,705.58	76,843,471.94	756,459.95	5,901,231.50	76,781,390.20	27.15	(4,474.08)
May 93	47	2,493,687.07	8,399,392.65	79,337,159.01	2,490,977.74	8,392,209.24	79,272,367.94	(2,709.33)	(7,183.42)
Jun 93	48	731,704.05	9,131,096.70	80,068,863.06	718,650.03	9,100,859.27	79,991,017.97	(13,054.02)	(20,237.43)
Jul 93	49	159,160.22	9,290,256.92	80,228,023.28	161,069.34	9,271,928.61	80,152,087.31	1,909.12	(18,328.31)
Aug 93	50	348,100.59	9,638,357.51	80,576,123.87	345,142.23	9,617,070.84	80,497,229.54	(2,958.36)	(21,286.67)
Sep 93	51	136,548.57	9,774,906.08	80,712,672.44	136,895.80	9,753,966.64	80,634,125.34	347.23	(20,939.44)
Oct 93	52	166,410.64	9,941,316.72	80,879,083.08	166,329.36	9,920,296.00	80,800,454.70	(81.28)	(21,020.72)
Nov 93	53	180,932.23	10,122,248.95	81,060,015.31	178,597.52	10,098,893.52	80,979,052.22	(2,334.71)	(23,355.43)
Dec 93	54	(26,776.80)	10,095,472.15	81,033,238.51	(26,502.56)	10,072,390.96	80,952,549.66	274.24	(23,081.19)
Jan 94	55	(671.38)	(671.38)	81,032,567.13	(660.12)	(660.12)	80,951,889.54	11.26	11.26
Feb 94	56	102,015.76	101,344.38	81,134,582.89	98,667.81	96,007.69	81,050,557.35	(3,347.95)	(3,336.69)
Mar 94	57	(15,193.84)	86,150.54	81,119,389.05	(14,695.21)	83,312.48	81,035,862.14	498.63	(2,838.06)
Apr 94	58	3,550,850.00	3,637,000.54	84,670,239.05	0.00	83,312.48	81,035,862.14	(3,550,850.00)	(3,553,688.06)
May 94	59	(414,780.85)	3,222,219.69	84,255,458.20	3,664,671.56	3,747,984.04	84,700,533.70	4,079,452.41	525,764.35
Jun 94	60	480,802.17	3,703,021.86	84,736,260.37	(64,338.05)	3,683,645.99	84,636,195.65	(545,140.22)	(19,375.87)
Jul 94	61	(74,139.12)	3,628,882.74	84,662,121.25	(71,707.42)	3,611,938.57	84,564,488.23	2,431.70	(16,944.17)
Aug 94	62	0.00	3,628,882.74	84,662,121.25	0.00	3,611,938.57	84,564,488.23	0.00	(16,944.17)
Sep 94	63	0.00	3,628,882.74	84,662,121.25	0.00	3,611,938.57	84,564,488.23	0.00	(16,944.17)
Oct 94	64	0.00	3,628,882.74	84,662,121.25	0.00	3,611,938.57	84,564,488.23	0.00	(16,944.17)
Nov 94	65	0.00	3,628,882.74	84,662,121.25	0.00	3,611,938.57	84,564,488.23	0.00	(16,944.17)
Dec 94	66	0.00	3,628,882.74	84,662,121.25	0.00	3,611,938.57	84,564,488.23	0.00	(16,944.17)
Jan 95	67	0.00	0.00	84,662,121.25	0.00	0.00	84,564,488.23	0.00	0.00
Feb 95	68	0.00	0.00	84,662,121.25	0.00	0.00	84,564,488.23	0.00	0.00
Mar 95	69	0.00	0.00	84,662,121.25	0.00	0.00	84,564,488.23	0.00	0.00
Apr 95	70	0.00	0.00	84,662,121.25	0.00	0.00	84,564,488.23	0.00	0.00
May 95	71	0.00	0.00	84,662,121.25	0.00	0.00	84,564,488.23	0.00	0.00
Jun 95	72	156,643.29	156,643.29	84,818,764.54	149,961.43	149,961.43	84,714,449.66	(6,681.86)	(6,681.86)
Jul 95	73	(23,329.85)	133,313.44	84,795,434.69	(22,334.68)	127,626.75	84,692,114.98	995.17	(5,686.69)
Total cashflowed		84,795,434.69	84,795,434.69	84,795,434.69	84,692,114.98	84,692,114.98	84,692,114.98		
Uncashflowed funds		20,127,565.31	20,127,565.31	20,127,565.31	20,230,885.02	20,230,885.02	20,230,885.02		
Totals		104,923,000.00	104,923,000.00	104,923,000.00	104,923,000.00	104,923,000.00	104,923,000.00		

APPENDIX 3.7 CASH FLOW/EXPENDITURE HISTOGRAMS

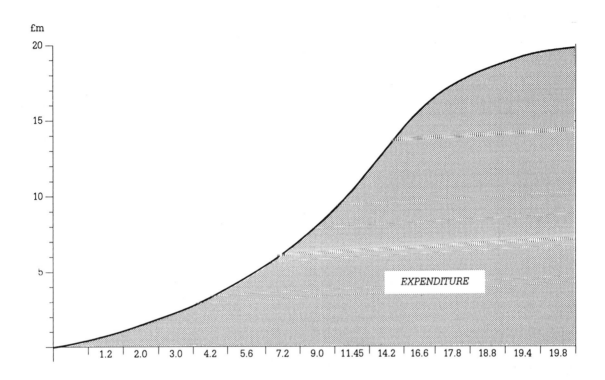

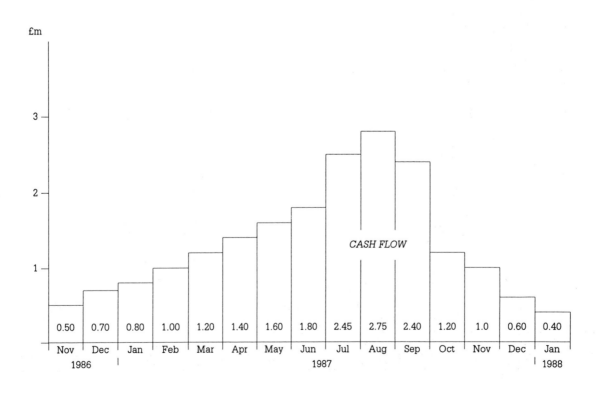

APPENDIX 3.8 COST CONTROL – CHECKLIST

- The objective of cost control is to allow the project to be completed within the approved budget. Cost reporting will facilitate at all times the best possible estimate of:

  — the final cost of the project;

  — the future cash flow;

  — the costs in the use of the completed facility.

- Monitoring expenditure to date does not exert any control over future expenditure and, hence, the final cost of the project. Effective cost control is only obtained when the whole of the Project Team has the correct attitude to cost control, ie one which will enable fulfilment of the Client's objectives.

  Effective cost control will require the following actions to be taken:

- Establishing that all decisions taken during design and construction are based on a forecast of the cost implications of the alternatives being considered, and that no decisions are taken whose cost implications would cause the total budget to be exceed, including appropriate contingency allowances.

- Encouraging the Professional Team to design within the cost plan and adopt the variation control procedure for the project, which is based on Architect's Instructions. No member of the team has the authority to increase costs on its section of the work. Increased costs on one item must be balanced by savings on another.

- Regularly amending and re-issuing the cost plan and variation orders causing an alteration to the brief.

- Adjusting the cash flow plan resulting from an alteration in the target cost, the master programme or the forecast of inflation.

- Developing the cost plan in liaison with the Professional Team as design and construction progresses. At all times it should comprise the best possible estimate of the final cost of the project and of the future cash flow. Development also means adding detail as more information about the work is assembled, replacing cost forecasts with more accurate ones or actual costs whenever better information can be obtained. Reviewing contingency and risk allowances at intervals is essential. Development of the cost plan should not involve increasing the total cost.

- Ensuring that the variation control procedure is strictly followed at all stages of the project. Only during the construction phase, when it can be demonstrated that significant delay, cost or danger would have been incurred by awaiting responses to the proposal from interested parties, may the procedure be carried out retrospectively. In this situation the matter must be discussed as fully as possible and a Site Instruction issued.

- Arranging that the contractor is given the correct information at the correct time in order to minimise claims. Any expected claims should be reported to the Client and included in the regular cost reports.

- Contingency money should be used only to pay for events which are unforeseen and unforeseeable. It should not be used to cover changes in the specification or in the Client's requirements or for variations resulting from errors or omissions. Should the Professional Team consider that there is no alternative but to exceed the budget, a written request to the Client must be submitted. This must include the following:

  — details of variations leading to the request;

  — confirmation that the variations are essential;

  — confirmation that compensating savings are not possible without having an unacceptable effect on the function of the completed project.

- Ensuring that regular, up-to-date and accurate cost reports are issued to the Client so that he is well informed of the current budgetary and cost situation. (*See* Appendix 3.6.)

- Establishing that all parties are clear about the meaning of each entry in the cost report. No data may be incorrectly entered into the report or incorrect deductions made from it.

- Ascertaining that the project costs are always reported back against the original approved budget. Any subsequent variations to the budget must be clearly indicated in the cost reports.

- Plots of predicted cash flow and actual one may be used to give a good indication of the project's progress. (*See* Appendix 3.7.)

APPENDIX 3.9 COST AND VARIATION CONTROL PROCEDURE

The procedure outlined is used to control the development of the project design from the design brief to preparation of tender documents. It will include:

- Addressing issues in the design brief.

- Variations from the design brief, including Design Team variations and Client variations.

- Developing details consistent with the design brief.

- Approving key design development stages, viz scheme design approval and detailed design approval.

The procedure is based on the Design Development Control Sheet (Appendix 3.10). The approved design will comprise the design brief and the full set of approved Design Development Control Sheets.

The procedure comprises the following stages:

- The appropriate member of the Design Team addressing each design issue in the development of the brief, co-ordinated by the Design Team Leader.

- Proposals developed are discussed with the appropriate members of the project's core group through submission of detailed reports/meetings, co-ordinated by the Project Manager. Reports should not repeat the design brief, but expand it, address an issue and prepare a change.

- Preparing a Design Development Control Sheet co-ordinated by the Design Team leader, giving:

  — design brief section and page references;

  — a statement of the issue;

  — a statement of the options;

  — the cost plan item, reference and current cost;

  — the effect on the cost plan of the recommendation;

  — a statement as to whether the recommendation requires transfer of Client contingency (ie a Client variation to the brief) and if so, the amount to be transferred;

- The Design Team report section of the control sheet is signed by:

  — the Design Team member responsible for recommendations;

  — the quantity surveyor; for cost effect;

  — the design team leader; for co-ordination;

- The Design Team leader sends the Design Development Control Sheet to the Project Manager who obtains the Client's approval signature and returns it to the Design Team leader.

- The quantity surveyor incorporates the effect of the approved recommendation into the cost plan.

APPENDIX 3.10 DESIGN DEVELOPMENT CONTROL SHEET

CLIENT NAME
PROJECT NAME

SHEET NO.

DESIGN TEAM REPORT

    Design brief section: Pages:
    Issue:

    Options considered: 1.
                                   2.
                                 3.

    Recommendation:

    Cost Plan Item:
    Ref:
    Current Cost:

    Effect of recommendation on costs/programmes:
    Increase/Decrease

    Application for transfer of Client
    contingency   Yes/No   Amount:

Architect/Services Engineer/Structural Engineer: Date:

Quantity surveyor: Date:

Design Team leader: Date:

CLIENT APPROVAL

Design development/Client contingency transfer approved. (Delete as applicable)

Position   *Signature*   *Date*

    ....

    ....

    ....

4. PRE-CONSTRUCTION STAGE

Once the Client has made a commitment to the project and accepted the feasibility report the project can proceed to the pre-construction phase. This will involve detailed design, preparation of tender documents, the tendering process and the production of enough working drawings to permit construction to start.

At the commencement of the pre-construction stage a number of key issues will have been decided:

- The Client's brief covering the type and nature of the project has been completed.

- A suitable site has been identified and made available.

- A Master Programme has been prepared.

- A cost allowance has been allocated to cover on-site development, including pre-main construction works, infrastructure, buildings, fit-out and equipment.

- Geological and topographical surveys of the site have been carried out.

- Planning authorities have been consulted regarding the planning status of the site, which is deemed acceptable for the intended purpose. Outline planning consent has been obtained.

- Statutory authorities, public bodies and utilities have been approached for information regarding all mains services, highways and related infrastructure items, which are likely to influence site development.

- A Professional Team has been appointed to provide – at least part of – the services required.

- The Client has authorised the project to proceed and should be aware that considerable costs will be incurred. These will not only include fees for professional services provided by the architect, quantity surveyor, Project Manager and structural engineer, but also planning fees and possibly costs associated with on-site detailed soil investigations, demolition, site clearance and other necessary activities specific to the site concerned.

- With large and complex projects a core group will have been formed consisting of the principal team members and the Client, all of whom will contribute to strategic decision taking.

- The Project Manager has prepared the Project Handbook in draft form and submitted it to the Client (*See* Part 3) and any other party concerned for comment, discussion and agreement. The Handbook will be finalised by the Project Manager and copies issued to nominated persons who are listed in the 'Parties to the Project'. The review and updating of the Handbook is the responsibility of the Project Manager.

ACTION PLANNING

The Project Manager will need to convene a meeting of the Professional Team and any other consultants/advisers to review all aspects of the project to date. A dossier of relevant information should be circulated in advance. A meeting of the parties concerned will follow later to formulate an action plan.

PROJECT CO-ORDINATION AND PROGRESS MEETINGS

Arranging and convening project progress meetings at relevant intervals to review progress on all aspects of the project and initiating action by appropriate parties to ensure that programmes and budgets are maintained is a further responsibility of the Project Manager. Distributing minutes of meetings to all concerned is an essential part of the follow-up action. (Appendix 4.1 provides details of the contents of a typical Agenda and Minutes.)

DESIGN TEAM MEETINGS

Team meetings are convened, chaired and minuted by the Design Team leader. It is not essential for the Project Manager to attend all team meetings as a matter of course, although normally having the right to do so. The Project Manager will receive minutes of all meetings and will report to the Client accordingly.

MONITORING PROFESSIONAL TEAM ACTIVITIES (*see* Figure 4.1)

The Project Manager is responsible for:

- Monitoring the project brief, programme and budget in association with the team. This is essential in view of their inter-relationship. However, effective inter-relationship cannot be finalised until the full team has been appointed and had time to get to grips with the project and its complexities.

- Advising the Design Team leader of the requirement to agree the detail and integration of the Design Team activities and to submit an integrated design production programme for co-ordination by the Project Manager.

- Incorporating, into the project programme, dates for the submission of design reports and periods for their consideration and approval.

- Commissioning, as necessary, or arranging for the team to commission, specialist reports, eg relating to the site, legal opinions on easements and restrictions and similar matters.

Figure 4.1 Professional Team's activities

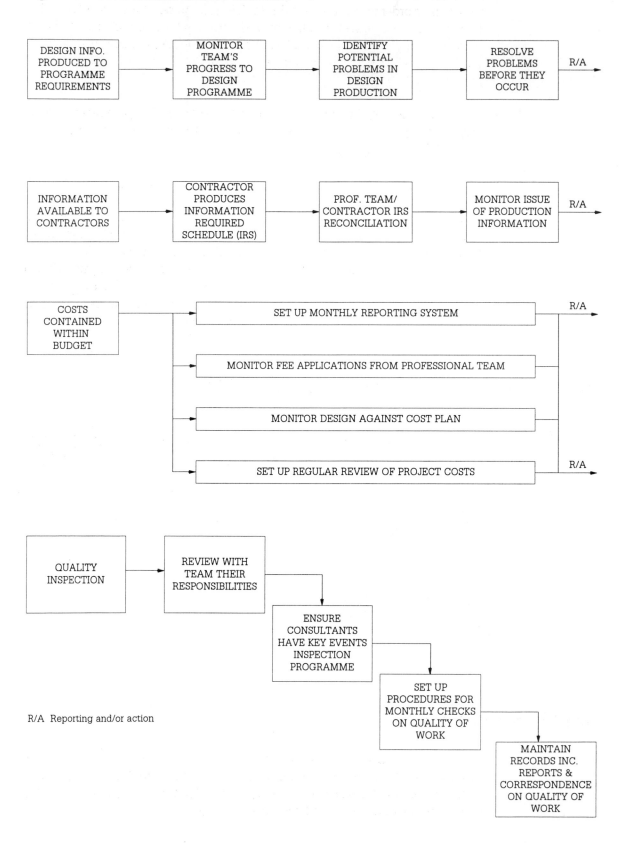

R/A Reporting and/or action

- Arranging for the team to be provided with all the information they require from the Client in order to execute their duties. It is an important function of the Project Manager to co-ordinate the activities of the various (and sometimes numerous) participants in the total process. Solicitors, accountants, tax advisers, development advisers, insurance brokers and others may all be involved in the pre-construction stage.

- Submitting, in conjunction with the Design Team leader, preliminary design proposals, reports and scheme design drawings to the Client for approval (*see* Figure 4.2).

- Conveying approvals to the team to proceed to subsequent stages of the project.

- Obtaining regular financial/cost reports and monitoring against budget/cost plans. Initiating remedial action within the agreed brief if the cost reports show that the budget is likely to be exceeded. Solutions to problems which cannot be resolved within the agreed brief, or likely substantial budget underspend, should be submitted to the Client with recommendations. The necessity to agree firm budget(s) at an early stage is most essential. It could, in certain cases, lead to some of the Client's preferred options being modified or even dropped from the brief.

Figure 4.2 Professional Team outline design proposals

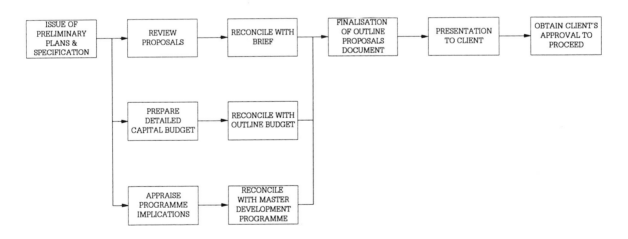

STATUTORY CONSENTS

Although a great deal of the detailed work involved in obtaining statutory consents, such as planning permission and Building Regulations approval is carried out by the Professional Team, the Project Manager has a vital facilitating role to play in what can be critical project activities.

- Monitoring the emerging detail design against the cost plan.

- Liaising with the Client/Project Team and the local authority/utilities and other statutory bodies for the obtaining of permissions and approvals.

- Evaluating changes in Client's requirements for cost and time implications and incorporating approved items into the design process.

- Monitoring progress and providing regular reports incorporating information relating to:

  — project status;

  — progress against programme, together with exceptions report;

  — cost against budget/cost plan, together with reconciliation statement;

  — forecast of total cost and date of completion;

  — critical areas;

  — corrective action needed.

- Obtaining the Client's approval to the detailed design and production information phase.

- Initiating arrangements for implementation of approved design and production information, to ensure that contractors' reasonable information requirements are fulfilled.

CLAIMS AND DISPUTES

The Project Manager should make every effort to pre-empt any claim or dispute that may arise and endeavour to mitigate and resolve the problem.

In the event of a claim or dispute, subject to the conditions of the contract, the application of 'Alternative Dispute Resolution' (ADR) may prove to be advantageous and is recommended as it provides:

— a viable method of early resolution to avoid claims and likely high costs;

— a conciliation service at short notice;

— a third party (ie adjudicator) free of any conflict or interest leading, generally, to a negotiated settlement.

An outline of procedures to be applied in checking contractual claims is given in Figure 4.5.

Figure 4.5 Claims procedure checklist

Records

All members of the Project Team must keep adequate records to check any claims.

These should include:

- Areas and materials available but work not in hand.

- Actual effect of significant Architect's Instructions on construction methods and programme.

- Date and content of requests for information.

- Date and content of information provided.

- Details of material deliveries.

- Dates of work in progress.

- List of errors and unsatisfactory work.

- Labour and supervision data.

- Weather conditions.

- Agreed progress reports backed (if possible) by photographs.

- Any disputed items.

Correspondence

- All claim-associated correspondence must be copied to the Project Manager and members of the Project Team concerned.

- All disputed statements and questions must receive comprehensive replies on the assumption that any letter may form part of a claim.

- The Architect/Contract Administrator/Supervising Officer will have the responsibility under the contract for dealing with claims. Discharging these duties will require building up adequate documentation.

- The Project Team should record, by correspondence, all important aspects of the conduct of the contract and not rely on minutes of meetings or site diaries records.

APPENDIX 4.1. MEETINGS AGENDA AND MINUTES

Agenda

- Heading: Group/Team designation and meeting's no/ref.

- Date, time, location.

- Introductions (if any) and apologies for absence.

- Prior action and/or submissions required.

- Reports, eg:

  — project brief;

  — design information;

  — procurement status;

  — pre-construction, construction and follow-up stages progress, including resourcing and potential problems;

  — achievement of key dates;

  — financial planning and controls;

  — health, safety and environmental protection;

  — labour relations.

Note: Reports required will depend on and relate to the Group/Team objectives.

- Any other business.

- Date and location of next meeting.

- Distribution/circulation list.

Minutes

- Heading (as for Agenda).

- Date, time and venue.

- Apologies for absence.

- Participants and chairman.

- Acceptance of and amendments/corrections to previous meeting minutes.

- Matters arising.

- Brief version of reports/discussions on items of the agenda and assignment of party/parties required to take action with relevant dates.

- Date, time and venue of next meeting.

- Distribution/circulation list.

5. CONSTRUCTION

The change from the pre-construction to the construction stage is a watershed. Work on site commences and it is necessary for the Professional Team, under the Project Manager's guidance to take stock and prepare for this dynamic period. The Project Manager's tasks in doing this are as follows:

- Establishing and implementing effective monitoring and control systems as specified in the Project Handbook, to ensure that the input of the Project Team (contractors, Design Team and consultants) meets the Client's objectives in terms of time, cost, specification and quality standards.

- Reviewing, in conjunction with the Project Team, project strategy, programmes, all relevant procedures/controls and completion of pre-construction works and checking their readiness for the commencement of main construction.

- Amending the Project Handbook, as and when appropriate, issuing amendments to parties concerned (*see* Appendix A) and overseeing adherence, throughout the project, to all procedures and provisions specified therein.

- Obtaining the contractor(s) preliminary programme before construction work starts, checking against the Master Programme and agreeing any necessary modifications jointly with the Professional Team.

It should be confirmed that:

- the construction supervisory staff (eg clerk(s) of work, resident engineer(s)), have well-defined, and fully understood, duties, responsibilities/authorities and lines of communication;

- existing site conditions, including adjacent properties, have been checked and details recorded, and that possession of the site can be given to the contractor on the due date, and that conditions and access conform with the description in the contract documents;

- site facilities are and will be maintained to the specified standards, and that safety, health and environmental protection requirements are satisfied, and security provisions arranged;

- all relevant contracts, including collateral warranties and performance bonds, are in place;

- all risk insurances, and those covering existing and adjacent properties, are in force.

- Arranging adequate project management support resourcing, eg planning, financial and administrative/clerical functions.

- Agreeing, in conjunction with the Professional Team:

  — contractor(s)' programmes, construction and design requirements;

  — adequacy of planned resources to achieve the programme;

  — any sub-letting in accordance with the contract(s) provisions.

- Maintaining, following initial approvals, contact with and involvement of local and other relevant authorities, in order to facilitate final approvals.

- Monitoring design and construction processes to see that:

  — adequate and timely information is available to contractor(s) and that their reasonable requests are met;

  — production information is available in accordance with programme requirements and that approval of contractors' drawings/specifications is given within the time limits;

  — costs are contained within the cost plan/budget;

  — the overall development objective and detailed programmes are achieved, (eg meeting progress, specifications and quality targets);

  — works supervision and inspection are carried out by parties concerned in accordance with the condition of their contracts/agreements.

- Arranging for and attending as appropriate, project meetings (eg as chairman, secretary, observer) and checking that accurate minutes/reports/action plans are produced and acted upon.

- Setting up procedures for dealing with claims and their processing, ie:

  — in accordance with conditions of contract (eg claimant specifying relevant clause(s) and giving full particulars in support of claim);

  — as they occur and within the time limit specified by the contract conditions, rather than at the end of the project;

  — daywork sheets rejected by construction supervisory staff are fully discussed and dealt with at the time, by the Project Manager, in conjunction with the Professional Team member(s), and the contractor concerned, preventing their 'storage' for later use in a claim or in a re-application;

  — assisting Professional Team members concerned in the verification of claims (*see* Figure 4.5).

- Monitoring and controlling variations which result from changes to the project brief to be avoided whenever possible (*see* Figure 5.1) or design/programme modification (eg Client's request, architect's or site instructions) must follow a procedure which:

  — identifies all consequences of the variation involved;

  — takes account of the relevant contractual provisions;

  — defines a cost limit, above which Client must be consulted and, similarly, when specifications or completion dates are affected;

  — authorises all variations only through a change order system initiated by the Project Manager. (*See* 'Variations and Instructions' on p. 121 and Figure 5.2 for changes in the Client's brief and Appendix 5.1. for an example of a Change Order pro-forma.)

Figure 5.1 Changes in the Client's brief

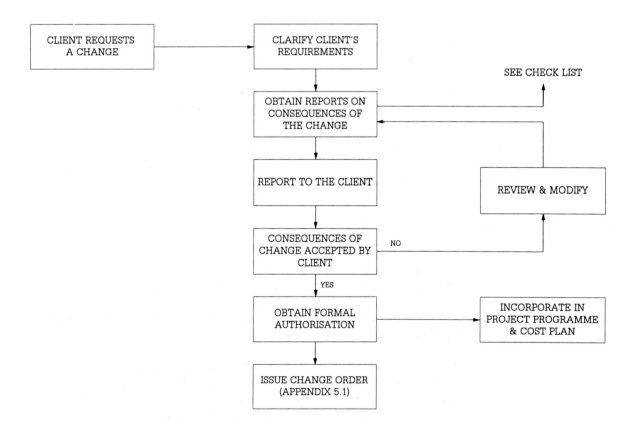

Figure 5.2 Changes in the Client's brief – checklist

Item	Action by
1. Request for change received from Client.	Project Manager
2. Client's need clarified and documented.	Project Manager
3. Details conveyed to Professional Team (Design Team and consultants).	Project Manager
4. Review of technical implications.	Professional Team & Project Manager
5. Assessment of programme implications.	Planning Support staff & Project Manager
6. Evaluation/calculation of cost implications.	Quantity Surveyor
7. Preparation of report on effect of change.	Project Manager in consultation with Professional Team
8. Reporting to Client.	Project Manager
9. Consequences accepted/not accepted by Client.	Project Manager
10. Non-acceptance – Further review/considerations as per item 4, 5, 6 and action items 7 & 8.	Professional Team & Project Manager
11. Further reporting to and negotiation of final outcome with Client.	Project Manager assisted by Professional Team members
12. Agreement reached and formal authorisation obtained.	Project Manager
13. Incorporation into Project programme and cost plan (budget).	Project Manager, Quantity Surveyor
14. 'Change Order' issued (sample forms – Appendix 5.1).	Project Manager & Client

- Identifying, in consultation with the Project Team, actual or potential problems and providing solutions which are within the time and cost limits and do not compromise the Client's requirements, with whom solutions are discussed and approval obtained.

- Checking the receipt of scheduled and/or 'ad hoc' reports, information and progress data from Project Team members.

- Submitting all regular and 'as requested' reports to the Client which are copied to other parties concerned, including:

  — project progress – status of design and construction;

  — notice of any further decisions required;

  — cost and budget controls, usually produced as a 'Financial Management Document' (*see* Appendix 3.6).

  — problems and measures to overcome them;

  — up-date on anticipated final cost and completion date.

  Detailed breakdown of reporting system is given in 'Cost control and reporting' and 'Planning programmes and progress reporting' on pages 130 and 132. (A summary of the contents of a Client report is given in Figure 5.3. and notes for guidance at Appendix 5.2.)

Figure 5.3 Regular reports to the Client – checklist of contents

CONTENTS

1. Executive summary.

2. Contractual arrangements including legal agreements.

3. Client's brief and requirements.

4. Client change requests.

5. Planning, Building Regulations and Fire Officer consents.

6. Public utilities.

7. Design reports – summaries.

8. Project Master Programme.

9. Tendering report.

10. Construction report – summary – including major sub-contractors.

11. Construction Programme.

12. Financial report – summary.

APPENDICES

1. Design reports in full.

2. Construction report in full.

3. Financial report in full.

4. Minutes of the meeting which received the previous report.

- Monitoring and processing, for the Client's action, all applications from Project Team members for interim and final payments, together with any other invoices.

- Monitoring, through the Professional Team, the contractor(s)' control of quality exercised in all operations on site and confirming that it is in accordance with the contract (*see* Figure 5.4).

Figure 5.4 *Management of quality*

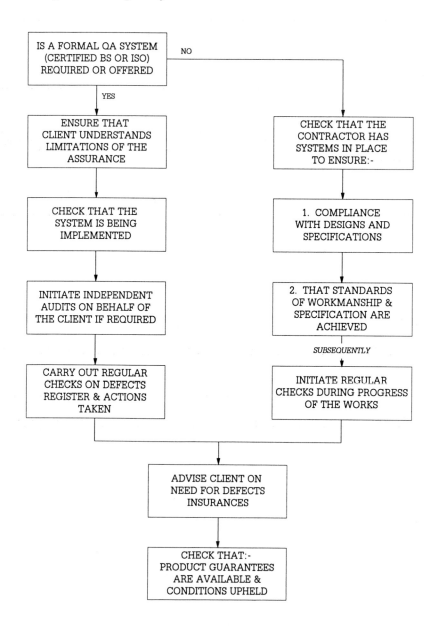

APPENDIX 5.1 CHANGE ORDER FORM

Project No.	Date	No.	'Project Management Ltd'
CLIENT: PROJECT:			DISTRIBUTION:

Subject – Definition of Change:	WHAT

Raised By:	WHO

Reasons for Change:	WHY

	Discretionary		Non-Discretionary	

COST AND TIME ASSESSMENT:

Recommended Action:

Draw From Reserve (Contingency) £

Transfer to Reserve (Contingency) £   .... Pr. Mgr. .... Date

Client Authorisation: Date:

Projected Programme and
Cost Plan (budget) amended on .... Pr. Mgr.

APPENDIX 5.2 REGULAR REPORTS TO CLIENT

Notes for guidance on contents

Executive Summary

The purpose of the Executive Summary is to give the Client a 'snapshot' of the project on a particular date which can be absorbed in a few minutes. It should contain short precise statements on the following:

a) significant events that have been achieved;

b) significant events that have not been achieved and action being taken;

c) significant events in the near future, particularly where they require specific action;

d) progress against the development, design and construction programmes;

e) financial status of the project.

Contractual arrangements (including legal agreements)

Each project requires the Client to enter into a number of legal agreements with parties such as local authorities, funding institutions, purchasers, tenants, consultants and contractors.

The report should be sub-divided to identify each particular agreement and to provide details of requirements and progress made against original development programme.

The following are indications of possible legal agreements that may be required on a project:

- Joint Development Agreement;

- Land Purchase Agreement;

- Funding Agreement;

- Purchase Agreement;

- Tenant/Lease Agreement;

- Consultants' Appointments;

- Town and Country Planning Acts sections in force at the time, eg:
  - planning gain;
  - highways agreement;
  - planning notices;
  - land adoption agreement;
  - public utilities diversion contract(s).

Client's brief and requirements

This provides a 'status' report on how the Client's brief and requirements are progressing. The report should identify any requirements which need clarification or amplification and also those which are still to be defined by the Client.

Client change requests

Client-originated changes should be listed under status ('being considered', 'in progress' or 'completed'), cost and programme implications. The objective is to make the Client fully aware of the impact and progress of any change.

Planning, Building Regulations and Fire Officer consents

This section will be sub-divided into the various consents required on a specific project. Each section should highlight progress made, problems, possible solutions and action required or in progress. The following are examples of possible consents:

- planning – outline;
- planning – detailed, including conditions;
- Building Regulations;
- means of escape;
- English Heritage/Historic Buildings;
- Fire Officer;
- Public Health;
- Environmental Health;
- Party Wall awards.

Public utilities

Each separate utility should be dealt with in terms of commitment, progress, completion and any agreements, wayleaves as appropriate.

Design reports – summaries

Design Team and consultants should prepare report(s) on progress problems and solutions which will form the appendices and must include marked-up design programmes and 'issue of information' schedules.

The design report, however, should be 'distilled' into an 'impact-making' synopsis and agreed as a fair representation by each member concerned.

Project Master Programme

Updated programmes should form an appendix to the report, specifying progress made. A short commentary on any noteworthy aspects should be made under this section.

Tendering report

This is a status report on events leading up to the acceptance of tenders. It should show clearly how the various stages are progressing against the action plan.

Construction report summary

This report is prepared in a similar way to that outlined for 'Design Reports' above.

Construction Programme

The updated programme should form an appendix to the report, highlighting progress made and showing where delays are occurring or are anticipated.

A short commentary on any important items should be given in the report under this section.

Financial report

A fully detailed financial report should form one of the appendices. It should provide a condensed overview (say two to three pages) giving the financial status and cash flow of the project. This report will embrace the information provided by the quantity surveyor and also call for the Project Manager to provide an overall financial view, highlighting any specific matters of interest to the Client.

Appendices

These will include full reports and programme updates as outlined in the previous sections. Other reports, possibly of a specialist nature, may also be included.

Should the report be presented at a formal meeting then the minutes of previous meetings should be included in the appendices.

6. FITTING OUT

Fitting out, as mentioned in Chapter 3 and as shown in Figure 3.2, can be carried out either under the terms of and as part of the main construction contract, or separately. Which course to adopt is determined at the feasibility and strategy stages and will depend on the project circumstances or Client requirements. In the case of a separate contract, eg by a user/tenant, the continuing role of the Project Manager in the co-ordination and supervision of the fitting-out phase needs to be established. All fitting-out requirements should be given full consideration and, as far as possible, be suitably provided for at the design, construction, completion and handover stages.

In the case of a separate contract a specific project Fitting-out Handbook is prepared by the Project Manager.

Generally, fitting-out comprises the following elements, which are implemented in a sequential order best suited to meet the required progress and the authorised cost plan.

Advice and assistance to the Client/Owner on:

— the preparation of heads of agreement for lease and lease;

— the preparation of material for and implementation of marketing or promotional campaigns;

— recommendations regarding contractual terms for the works to be carried out;

— preparation, in conjunction with the Professional Team, of drawings, specifications and relevant tender and contract documents;

— selection and appointment of suitable contractor(s);

— reviewing and reporting: (i) to all parties concerned and taking action where appropriate, including certification; (ii) agreements with the quantity surveyor on meeting schedules and valuation dates; (iii) on cost comparisons with the cost plan; (iv) on claims for extension of time in conjunction with the members of the Design Team and consultants concerned.

— monitoring: (i) information flow from the Professional Team; (ii) Client/Owner payments against interim certificates and fee payments to the Professional Team.

Completion of building/facility outstanding work generally involves the following stages:

— confirming availability for outstanding work;

— preparing a schedule of outstanding work, obtaining the relevant certificate of practical completion, obtaining acceptance of a works list and agreement for the programme of completion;

— acceptance by contractor of works programme;

— monitoring the effectiveness of works programme after issuing the relevant certificate of practical completion.

User/tenant liaison

— co-ordinating and facilitating provision of information to formulate fitting-out proposals;

— arranging Client/owner/tenant approval of proposals.

Contractor(s) liaison

— verifying insurance arrangements and local authority approval to start work;

— checking that effective system of information flow, communication, reporting and certification for all parties concerned is set up and that the relevant Project Handbook is either updated or that one is prepared;

— monitoring the preparation of designs and specifications, and their issue to contractor(s), including action on 'Information Required Schedules';

— reviewing and agreeing works programme, adequate resourcing, application of relevant regulations and special conditions, eg access and interface with any other working parties.

— monitoring: (i) progress against the Master Programme and initiating corrective action, if required; (ii) adherence to quality standards; (iii) compliance with regulations (statutory and local authority site visits) and Client/owner/tenant requirements; (iv) arrangements for testing and commissioning of all engineering services.

Financial considerations

— checking payments by Client/owner for any fit-out contribution;

— monitoring and recording any contra-charges from fit-out contractor(s);

— agreeing with Client/owner the contra-charges and any balancing payments.

7. COMMISSIONING, COMPLETION AND HANDOVER

The location of this chapter does not mean that the activities involved only take place at the end of the construction stage, as reference to Figure 7.1 will demonstrate. Each of these sub-sections require the Project Manager and others to address them much earlier in the project. In each case specific requirements will need to be built into the specifications and contract elements before tenders are invited or negotiation with contractors begin. Flow charts, schedules and check lists relating to the various stages within this chapter are given at Figures 7.2 to 7.6 and at Appendices 7.1 to 7.4.

INSPECTION, TESTING, SAMPLES, MOCK-UPS AND ACCEPTANCE

The Professional Team, in collaboration with the Project Manager, formulates recommendations to the Client/Owner in respect of:

— on and off-site inspection of work for compliance with specifications, and testing of materials and workmanship;

— performance testing and the criteria to be used;

— preparation of schedules for required samples and mock-ups, their updating and monitoring progress of approvals. Copies of schedules are included in the relevant monthly reports.

Professional Team members must:

— inspect, as appropriate, the work for which they have design responsibility and report to the Design Team leader, with copy to the Project Manager, on progress and compliance with contract provisions, highlighting any corrective action to be taken;

— inspect work at the practical completion phase, produce the outstanding work schedule and sign off, certifying, subject to completion of works listed in the schedule. As a general rule a certificate of practical completion should not be issued if there are incomplete or defective works outstanding;

— inspect the work at the end of the contract defects liability period, compile defects schedule and subsequently confirm that: (i) all defects have been rectified; (ii) any omissions have been made good; (iii) all necessary repairs have been carried out.

— complete their obligations to enable the contract to be finalised.

COMMISSIONING

Commissioning is carried out in two distinct parts:

Client Commissioning, which is an activity predominantly carried out by the Client's personnel assisted, where required, by the Professional Team.

Commissioning must be given consideration throughout the project, starting as early as the late phase of the strategy stage. Although it does not actually occur until the final stages of the project, its planning and preparation should take place much earlier.

Engineering services commissioning is part of the construction design and installation phases of the project and, in a traditional contract, is the responsibility of the main contractor and the services sub-contractor. The Design Team must take account at the pre-construction stage of the need to facilitate testing and performance evaluation.

The notional relationship between commissioning and other stages is shown in Figure 7.1.

Generally, the commissioning process objectives and main tasks are as described in the following sections.

Figure 7.1 Relationship between project stages

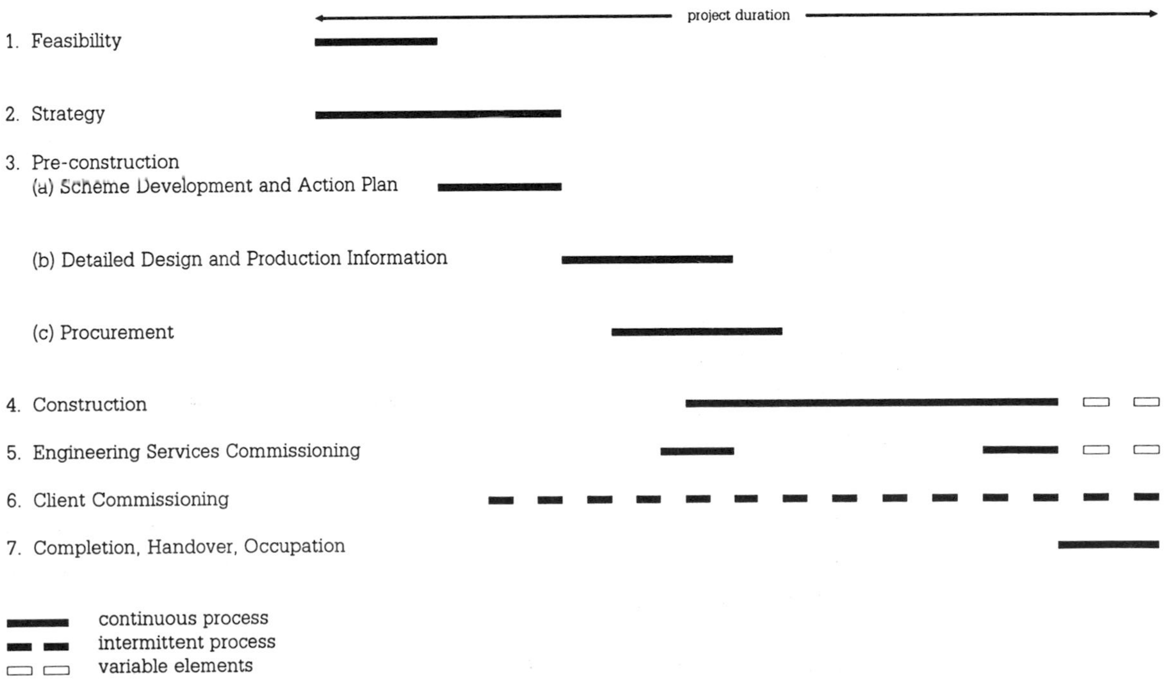

project duration

1. Feasibility

2. Strategy

3. Pre-construction
   (a) Scheme Development and Action Plan

   (b) Detailed Design and Production Information

   (c) Procurement

4. Construction

5. Engineering Services Commissioning

6. Client Commissioning

7. Completion, Handover, Occupation

continuous process
intermittent process
variable elements

- Ensuring that handover takes place when all statutory inspections and approvals are satisfactorily completed but does not take place if the Client/tenant cannot have beneficial use of the facility, ie, not before specified defects are 'made good', indicating likely consequences and drawbacks of premature occupation.

- Setting up procedures to monitor and supervise any post-handover works, which do not form part of the main contract, and to monitor the defects liability period.

- Initiating, in close co-operation with the Professional Team contra-charging measures in cases of difficulties with completing outstanding works or 'making good' defects.

- Monitoring progress of final accounts by assisting in any controversial aspects or disputes, and by ascertaining draft final accounts are available on time and are accurate.

Figure 7.2 Construction/building works checks, inspection and sign off

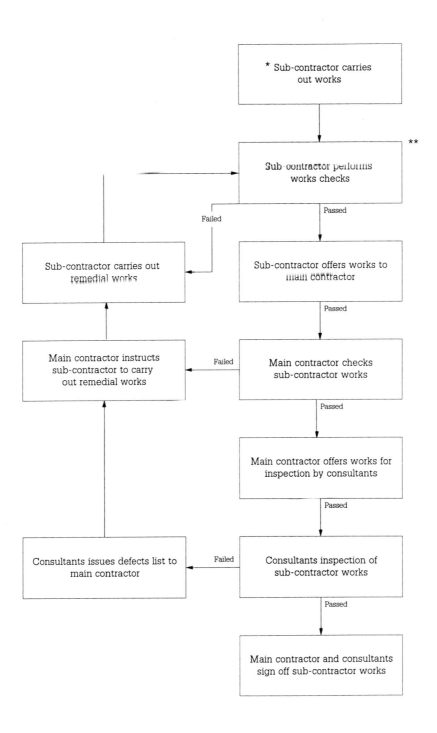

N.B. * The term 'sub-contractor' indicates specialist, or works or trade contractor
** can be undertaken by independent quality checking organisation

8. OCCUPATION (MIGRATION)

Occupation, as in the case of fitting-out, can be part of the main construction contract, or separate. A decision will be made at the feasibility and strategy stages, depending on the Client's objectives, and/or user's/tenant's requirements.

Unlike many other project management activities, occupation involves employees themselves and the style of management and culture of the user's organisation. Consequently, well executed planning and involvement process can result in better management/employee relations, bringing a greater feeling of involvement and commitment to the workforce.

The procedure outlined below gives a typical approach, which may need to be interpreted in order to harmonise with the practices and expectations of the user. Nevertheless, change in established practices is encouraged where doing so will smooth the process and make it more effective.

Occupation can be divided into four stages:

Structure for implementation

Appointment of individuals and groups to set out the necessary directions, consultation and budget/cost parameters.

Scope and objectives

Deciding what is to be done, considering the possible constraints and reviewing as necessary.

Methodology

How the whole process will be achieved. Identification of individual or group of special activities and their task lists aimed at defining the parameters and other related matters, eg financial implications.

Organisation and controls (the 'doing' stage)

Carrying out the process and keeping programme and budget/cost under review.

The individuals and groups likely to be concerned are:

- Project Executive: Appointed by the Client/tenant at the director/senior management level and responsible for the complete process.

- Occupation Co-ordinator: Project Manager appointed, or existing one confirmed by the 'Client', with 'on the spot' responsibility.

- Occupation steering group (A): Chaired by the Project Executive and consisting of Occupation Co-ordinator and a few selected senior representatives covering the main functional areas. Concerned with all major decisions but subject to any constraints laid down by the Client, eg financial limits.

- Senior representatives' meeting (B): Chaired by one of the functional representatives on the occupation steering group and made up of a few senior representatives covering the majority of employees and the occupation co-ordinator.

- Local representative groups (C): Chaired by manager/supervisor of own group and concerned with providing views related to a particular location or department. Membership to reflect the specific interest of the group at the location.

- Special activities meetings (D): Meetings for individual or group of special activities as identified in 'methodology'. A single person will be made responsible for achieving all the tasks which make up a special activity and will chair the respective meetings.

- Move group (E): Responsible for the overall direction of the physical move, having been delegated by the Occupation Steering Group, the task of detailed preparation and control of the move programme including its budget/cost.

- Briefing groups: Concerned with effective and regular communication with all employees to provide information to work groups/sections by their own managers or supervisors, so that questions for clarification are encouraged. Special briefings may, in addition, be vital especially during the Occupation (migration) build-up.

Figures 8.1 to 8.4 are intended to give 'at a glance' summary of the Occupation (migration) process and Appendix 8.1 provides checklists for a typical control system.

Figure 8.1 Occupation (migration) – structure for implementation

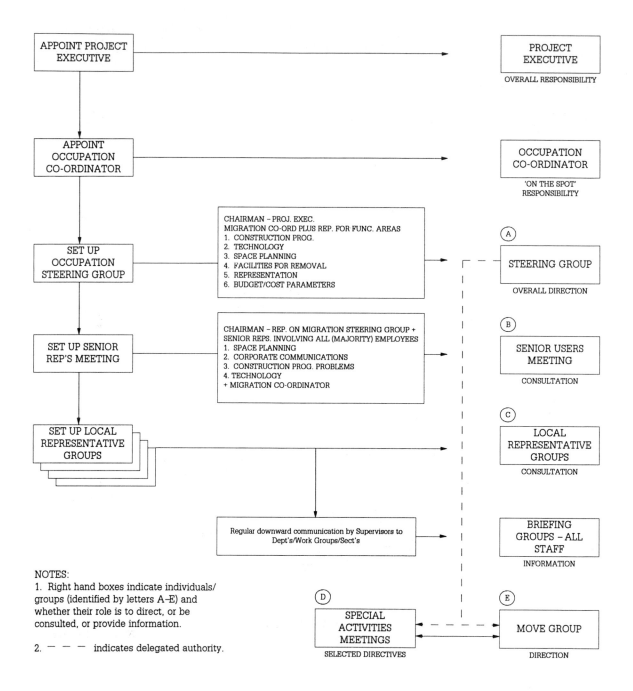

NOTES:
1. Right hand boxes indicate individuals/
groups (identified by letters A–E) and
whether their role is to direct, or be
consulted, or provide information.

2. – – – indicates delegated authority.

Figure 8.2 Occupation (migration) – scope and objectives

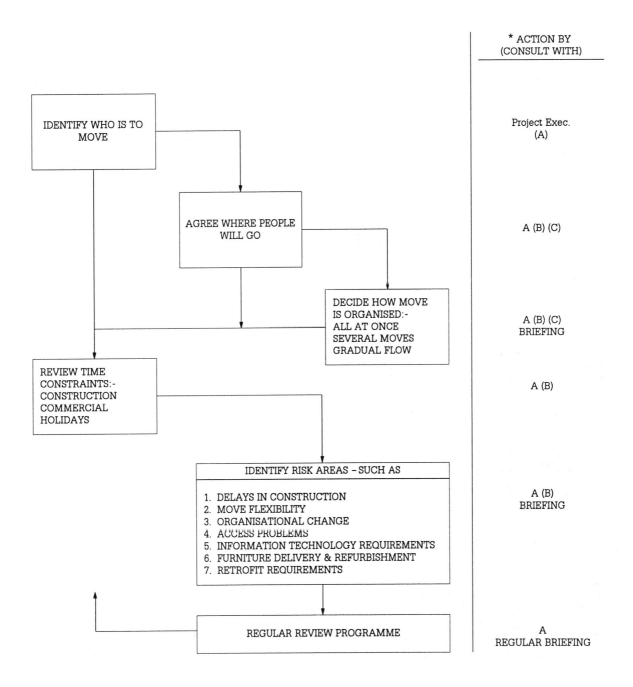

Figure 8.3 Occupation (migration) – methodology

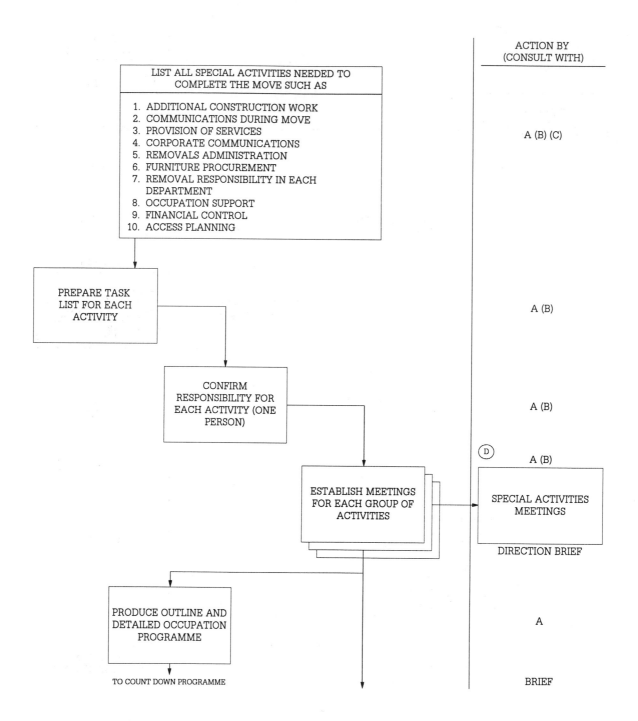

Figure 8.4 Occupation (migration) – organisation and control

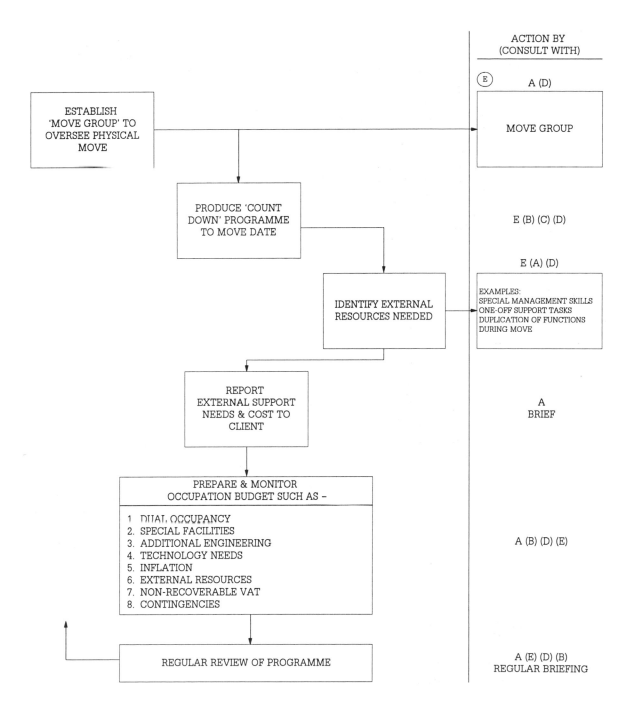

APPENDIX 8.1 CHECKLIST – OCCUPATION (MIGRATION)

Task	Direct Responsibility	To be consulted

Structure for implementation

1. Appoint:

Project Executive. Occupation Co-ordinator.	CLIENT	CLIENT

2. Establish Occupation Steering Group.

Chairman – Project Executive + Occupation Co-ordinator + Functional representatives	PROJECT EXECUTIVE	OCCUPATION CO-ORDINATOR

  1. Construction programme.
  2. Technology.
  3. Space planning.
  4. Facilities for removal.
  5. Representation Groups.
  6. Budget/Cost parameters.

Purpose – overall direction.

3. Establish Senior Representatives meeting.

Chairman – representative on Occupation Steering Group + Occupation Co-ordinator + senior representatives involving all (majority of) employees	PROJECT EXECUTIVE	OCCUPATION CO-ORDINATOR + SENIOR REPRESENT- ATIVE ON OCCUPATION STEERING GROUP

  1. Space planning.
  2. Corporate communications.
  3. Construction programme problems.
  4. Technology.

Purpose – consultation.

4. Set up local representatives groups for locations and/or departments.	OCCUPATION CO-ORDINATOR	SENIOR REPRESENTATIVES

Purpose – local consultation.

5. Ascertain existence of system for regular downward communications by manager or supervisor to own work group – face to face.

	OCCUPATION CO-ORDINATOR + LINE MANAGEMENT	SENIOR REPRESENT- ATIVE + LOCAL REPRESENTATIVE GROUPS

Purpose – keeping *all* employees informed.

Task	Direct Responsibility	To be consulted
Scope and objectives		
6. *Identify who is to move.*	PROJECT EXECUTIVE	(A)
7. *Agree where people will go in new location/s.*	A	(B), (C)
8. *Decide how moves will be organised.*	A	(B), (C)

- all at once;
- several moves;
- gradual flow.

9. *Review time constraints:*	A	(B)

- construction;
- commercial;
- holidays.

10. *Identify risk areas, such as:*	A	(B)

delays in construction;
migration flexibility;
organisational changes;
access problems;
information technology needs;
furniture delivery and refurbishment;
retrofit refurbishment requirements.

11. *Regularly review 6,7,8,9 & 10.*	A	

Methodology

12. *List all special activities needed to complete the move, eg.*	A	(B), (C)

additional building work;
communications during move;
provision of services;
corporate communications;
removals administration;
furniture procurement;
removal responsibility in each
location/department;
move support;
financial control;
access planning.

- Authorised and final cost.

- Planned against actual costs (eg 'S' curves) and analysis of original and final budget.

- Impact of claims.

- Maintenance of necessary records to enable the financial close of the project.

- Identification of time extensions and cost differentials resulting from amendments to original requirements and/or other factors.

- Brief analysis of original and final programme(s) including stipulated and actual completion date. Reasons for any variations.

HUMAN RESOURCES ASPECTS

- Communication channels and reporting relationships (bottle-necks and their causes).

- Industrial relations problems (if any).

- General assessment and comments on staff welfare, morale and motivation.

PERFORMANCE STUDY

- Planning and scheduling activities.

- Were procedures correct and controls effective?

- 'Man hours' summary:

  — breakdown of planned against actual;

  — sufficiency of resources to carry out work in an effective manner.

- Identification of activities performed in a satisfactory manner and those deemed to have been unsatisfactory.

- Performance rating (confidential) for future use, of the Professional Team and contractors.

10. SELECTIVE BIBLIOGRAPHY

The following is not intended to provide a comprehensive guide to the vast amount of literature available. Rather it is intended to support readers by directing them to supplementary titles which will allow Project Management to be evaluated and understood within its appropriate context.

CHARTERED INSTITUTE OF BUILDING (1988). Project management in building. Second edition.

GRAY, C & FLANAGAN, R (1989). The changing role of specialist and trade contractors.

CHARTERED INSTITUTE OF BUILDING (1983). Code of estimating practice. Fifth edition.

CHARTERED INSTITUTE OF BUILDING (1991). Planning and programming in construction.

FRANKS, J (1990). Building procurement systems. Second edition. Chartered Institute of Building.

MURDOCH, I & HUGHES, W (1992). Construction contracts: law and management E & F N Spon

CONSTRUCTION DISPUTES RESOLUTION GROUP (1991). Construction disputes: early settlement at low cost. ACE.

IABSE (1986). Organisation of the design process. Designer–contractor relationship. Workshop. Zurich.

HUGHES, W P (1991). An analysis of construction management contracts. CIOB Technical Information Service Paper No 135.

BRITISH PROPERTY FEDERATION (1983). Manual of the BPF system for building design and construction.

RICS (1992). Client guide to the appointment of a quantity surveyor.

ASSOCIATION OF CONSULTING ENGINEERS (1991). Good design is good investment; advice to client: selection of consulting engineer; and fee competition.

SCOTT, K L (1992). The management of contractual claims. Chartered Institute of Building.

ROUGVIE, A (1987). Project evaluation and development. B T Batsford.

LOCK, D (1988). Project management. Fourth edition. Gower.

WALKER, A (1989). Project management in construction. Second edition. BSP.

ACA (1988) Project team guidelines; fee negotiations and harmonised plan of work.

ASHFORD, J L (1989). The management of quality in construction. E & F N Spon.

RIBA INDEMNITY RESEARCH (1989). Quality assurance.

CHARTERED INSTITUTE OF BUILDING (1989). Quality assurance in the building process.

BENNETT, J (1985). Construction project management. Butterworths.

FOREWORD

The Project Management Agreement and Conditions of Engagement has been designed as a model Agreement and Conditions of Engagement to provide a widely-circulated basis for use by Clients and Project Managers. The Project Manager has only recently emerged as an independent professional and there are still wide differences of opinion as to the responsibilities he has and the services he provides.

This Agreement has been written on the basis of the generally recognised situation in the construction industry where the person or company in the position of Project Manager co-ordinates other consultants appointed directly by the Client. A distinction between project management and project co-ordination is made by RICS Insurance Services Limited. If the Project Manager appoints other consultants, RICSIS defines the service as project management. If the Client appoints other consultants, the service is defined as project co-ordination.

Appendix A has been left blank to enable the Client and Project Manager to agree the services to be provided and incorporate them into each Agreement. Appendices B–F have also been left blank for completion as indicated in the appropriate sections of this Guidance Note. A range of the services provided by chartered surveyors undertaking project management work is included in this guidance note. This is for use by the parties in developing a schedule of services appropriate to the Client's requirements and the ability and skills of the Project Manager.

It is important that the services required are clearly defined to remove uncertainty and to identify the responsibilities of both parties.

The document is based on English Law and advice should be taken if it is intended to use the document under any other legal jurisdiction.

A Scottish Edition titled *Project Management Contract of Engagement* is available for use in Scotland issued by the Royal Institution of Chartered Surveyors in Scotland.

The authors hope that the document will be used on a wide scale and welcome comments on any amendments which might be incorporated. These should be sent to: The Director, Planning and Development Division, Royal Institution of Chartered Surveyors, 12 Great George Street, London SW1P 3AD.

Published on behalf of
The Royal Institution of Chartered Surveyors
by Surveyors Holdings Limited
under the RICS Books imprint
12 Great George Street, London SW1P 3AD

Introduction

This agreement is divided into three main sections:

- Memorandum of Agreement
- Conditions of Engagement
- Appendices A to F

The Memorandum of Agreement contains a brief statement of the principal responsibilities and objectives of the parties and provides for completion of most of the variables of the contract.

The Conditions of Engagement states the main conditions of contract which will apply.

The Appendices allow the parties to include information relevant to the contract which is expected to vary to suit the requirements of the parties and the project.

It is anticipated that the Project Manager will frequently be appointed from the earliest phases of a project when the extent, nature, description and timescale have not been determined. The Agreement cannot be fully completed until sufficient development work on the Project has occurred to identify the brief, the extent of the involvement of the Project Manager and the probable timescale. It may be appropriate for the parties to rely on a partially completed Agreement supplemented by other documentation for final agreement when all necessary details are available.

Throughout this guidance note, Agreement, Conditions of Engagement and Appendices words expressed in the masculine include, where appropriate, the feminine.

Memorandum of Agreement

Complete the details of date, Client's name and address and Project Manager's name and address. Note that the name to be inserted is the project management organization.

NOTE: Take care to complete all clauses identified by an asterisk in the Memorandum of Agreement.

Clause A: Insert name and address of project in sufficient detail to clearly identify the project which is the subject of this Agreement.

Clause B: The Project Manager should clarify his fee position if the calculation is based on the assumption of a future appointment of a consultant. This clause does not place an obligation on the Client to appoint particular consultants.

Clause 8: Insert date of commencement of the Agreement.

Clause 9: Insert the period of delay for which the Project Manager is prevented from carrying out his Services. The purpose of this clause is to enable the project management organization to determine when it can commit its resources to other projects. A period of 12 months would be reasonable.

Clause 10(a): Insert the amount of the fee.

Clause 10(c): This is only to be completed if a lump sum fee is agreed. Insert the anticipated date for completion of the Project. It is expected that time committed to the project by the Project Manager will be affected by the delay of the project. If the Project is extended by agreement between the parties (see clause 7.5 of the Conditions), there is provision for the application of a predetermined formula in Appendix D.

Clause 10(d): Insert the rate of interest to be applied to invoices remaining unpaid after 28 days. See clause 7.2 and Appendix C of the Conditions. The figure could be a fixed figure or a percentage related to the current rate of a well known variable rate such as LIBOR. This figure should not be a penalty but a fair calculation of the cost to the Project Manager of an invoice remaining unpaid.

Clause 11: Insert the name of the principal person employed by the Project Manager to undertake the duties covered by this Agreement. Project management is seen to be a personal service relying greatly on the management skills of the individual as well as the organization — this clause has been included to reflect that importance. Note the provisions under clauses 3.2 and 3.3 of the Conditions for changing the named person under certain circumstances. Death or a change of employment may force the project management organization to seek consent for a change.

Clause 12: Insert the amount for which professional indemnity insurance is to be maintained for each claim. The amount must be agreed with the Client and may be required by a third party providing funding. The Project Manager should ensure that he continues to be adequately insured after the completion of the project.

Chartered surveyors should note that they are required under Bye Law 24(9)(A) to insure against claims for professional duty under an insurance policy which is no less comprehensive than the Professional Indemnity Collective Policy issued by RICS Insurance Services.

The Client may request a certified copy of the wording of the Project Manager's professional indemnity policy. This will provide the Client with details of the cover in place to assist in judging the extent of the liability that ought to be covered under Clause 6 (a) of the Memorandum of Agreement. No limit is provided for the duration of the insurance cover in this clause or clause 12 of the Memorandum of Agreement. The Project Manager is advised to maintain run-off cover in the event that he ceases trading. The requirement to maintain the level of cover after the completion of the project will make the intentions of the parties clear, but this could in some circumstances be difficult for the Client to enforce. Project Managers using this Agreement who are not chartered surveyors are advised to check that their professional indemnity policy is no less comprehensive than the RICS Professional Indemnity Collective Policy.

10 Construction economics and financial management

10.1 Advise on commissioning, capital and the life cycle cost studies of alternative designs and materials. Advise Client on energy budgeting. Arrange appropriate financial procedures for risk assessment and for tax provision.

10.2 Advise the Client on appropriate procedures for dealing with insurance claims and agree any changes required to Consultants' fee arrangements generated by them.

10.3 Check that the Consultants are providing adequate and timely information for the preparation of tender documentation.

10.4 Obtain Client authorization for costs of variations when limit of authority is exceeded and check that costs are being agreed.

10.5 Report to the Client at regular intervals giving forecast of final costs, including costs of variations and the cost implications of extensions of time, and forecast completion dates.

10.6 Check that Consultants prepare regular valuations and payment certificates of the contractors' works valued in accordance with the building contract. Check that valuations and certificates are correctly circulated.

10.7 Check, in conjunction with Consultants, fees for statutory approvals and arrange payments.

10.8 Check and recommend Consultants' applications for payment.

10.9 Check and recommend all other invoices related to the development.

10.10 Check that Consultants prepare final account and agree settlement.

10.11 Arrange for the Client to obtain advice on taxation implications.

11 Cash flow

11.1 In conjunction with Consultants, arrange for the preparation and maintenance of cash flow forecasts and statements for monitoring project expenditure.

11.2 Check and recommend payment of Client's copies of certificates. Authorize any other payments due and check against cash flow. Check Client makes payment within the stipulated time.

12 Local authority and planning approvals

12.1 Co-ordinate and support negotiations with planning authorities.

12.2 Check with the architect the form and content of planning applications. Progress the planning process and arrange that a check of all approval/refusal documents is carried out by the project team. Check that Consultants implement and deal with any conditions attached to a planning consent.

12.3 Check with the Consultants which other statutory approvals are required and that applications for approval are submitted. Check that Consultants apply for amendments to statutory approvals granted when required.

12.4 Check that the Consultants obtain clearance from health and safety and fire officers.

13 Contract procedures

13.1 Decide with Consultants the selection and method of appointment of preferred/nominated subcontractors and agree extent of design and specifications to be included in tender documents. Advise the Client accordingly.

13.2 Decide with Consultants procurement procedure for selection of contractors. Decide on type and form of contract. Monitor Consultants in the preparation and assembly of tender documents. With the Consultants, check the form and content.

13.3 With the Consultants, prepare list of tenderers, conduct interviews, if required, and obtain approval.

13.4 Arrange with Consultants tender analysis; obtain clarification of ambiguities and prepare tender report. If necessary, arrange interview of tenderers. Prepare tender award recommendation and obtain instructions.

13.5 Co-ordinate the preparation of contract documents. Arrange for preparation of Contractor's duty of care warranty if required. Arrange signatures of parties to the contract.

13.6 Arrange for the Contractor's insurance certificate and renewal of insurance at renewal dates to be checked.

14 Contract management

14.1 Arrange for Client to place orders for long-delivery components.

14.2 Advise Client of any works to be carried out under separate direct contract.

14.3 Co-ordinate the Consultants using reasonable endeavours to secure the provision of information to contractors in an appropriate timescale.

14.4 Check that Consultants are providing adequate supervision in accordance with their terms of appointment and undertaking regular site inspections.

14.5 Check that variations and instructions are being issued and correctly circulated.

14.6 Check that the Consultants fulfil their contractual

obligations in assessing and dealing with extensions of time and issuing the appropriate certificates.

14.7 Check that the Consultants fulfil their contractual obligations in confirming completion and issuing appropriate certificates of making good defects and completion.

15 Building management, commissioning and maintenance

15.1 Liaise with Client/agents on practical management, maintenance programmes, provision of maintenance staff, and state of services pending occupation.

15.2 With Consultants and contractors, arrange handover after operational tests and full commissioning of services.

15.3 Liaise with Client/agents/Consultants on commissioning and equipping programmes. Arrange for contractors' and Consultants' maintenance and cleaning information, maintenance manuals, test certificates, guarantees, operating instructions, 'as-built' drawings and 'as-installed' diagrams to be forwarded to the Client.

16 Tenancies and fitting out

16.1 With the Client and Consultants, prepare and implement a marketing or promotion campaign.

16.2 Liaise with Client/agents/solicitor in agreeing the terms of agreement for lease.

16.3 Procure the preparation of drawings, specifications or other documentation required for marketing or contracts.

16.4 Provide any tenant with information to enable him to prepare fitting out proposals and arrange for any client approvals to be obtained.

16.5 On behalf of the Client prepare any regulations necessary to control the undertaking of tenant's fitting out.

16.6 Check tenant's fitting out is monitored, and that the implementation and the completed works comply with client regulations and approvals.

16.7 Obtain copies of, or arrange issue of, certificates as appropriate relating to the tenant's fitting out.

Appendix B

The Client and Project Manager must agree all those matters which require the written consent of the Client under clause 6.2 before the Project Manager proceeds. This Appendix is important in determining the authority of the Project Manager to proceed without specific reference to the Client. Examples of matters that could be included follow:

- The variation of the design or specification of work relating to the Brief or accepted tenders
- Any amendment to the Contractors' contracts or obligations or waiver of compliance with same
- Any amendment to the Consultants' conditions of appointment or waiver of compliance with same
- The confirmation to the architect to issue any contract instruction over £ .... value
- The confirmation to the architect to issue any contract instructions or any other action that could be expected to delay completion of the Project beyond the agreed date
- The granting of assent to a Consultant to assign all or part of their appointment
- The granting of assent to a contractor to assign all or part of their work
- Any delegation of the duties ascribed to the Project Manager under this Agreement

Appendix C

The schedule of payments of the fee stated in clause 10(a) of the Memorandum of Agreement and referred to in clause 10(b) should be stated here. The schedule may, for example, be stated in percentages or amounts. The time due for payment may be stated by date or by project stage. Note that failure of the Client to pay within 28 days will attract interest on the amount due under clause 7.3 of the Conditions.

Appendix D

See the comments above under clause 10(c) of the Memorandum of Agreement. The parties must make clear the basis on which any adjustment to the fee will be made if the date of completion of the Project is delayed.

Appendix E

It is expected that the Project Manager's normal facilities would be provided as part of the agreed fee.

If any site office accommodation or special project offices are to be paid for by the Client and are not included in the fee stated in clause 10(a) of the Memorandum, they must be clearly stated in this Appendix.

Appendix F

Clause 10 of the Conditions provides for all disbursements and expenses to be included except those listed in this

Appendix. The parties should agree all items that will be invoiced in addition to the fee stated in clause 10(a) of the Memorandum.

A sample list of disbursements and expenses follows:

- Travel costs
- Taxi fares
- Car hire
- Document copying
- Printing
- Drawing reproduction
- Hotel accommodation
- Subsistence
- Telephones
- Telex
- Facsimile
- Postage
- Stationery
- Translation

MEMORANDUM OF AGREEMENT BETWEEN CLIENT AND PROJECT MANAGER

---

* MEMORANDUM OF AGREEMENT made the .... day of .... 19 ......

BETWEEN:

....

(hereinafter called 'the Client') of the one part

(of) (whose registered office is at) ....

....

and

....

(hereinafter called 'the Project Manager') of the other part

(of) (whose registered office is at) ....

....

WHEREAS

* **A** The Client intends to proceed with ....

....

....

(referred to in this Agreement as 'the Project') and has requested the Project Manager to provide professional services as referred to in the Conditions of Engagement and Appendices attached hereto (referred to in this Agreement as 'the Services'). Words expressed in the masculine in this Agreement, Conditions of Engagement and Appendices include, where appropriate, the feminine.

B The Client intends to appoint other consultants to provide other services in connection with the Project.

NOW IT IS HEREBY AGREED as follows:

1   The Client agrees to engage the Project Manager subject to and in accordance with the Conditions of Engagement attached hereto and the Project Manager agrees to provide the services set out in Appendix A subject to and in accordance with the said Conditions of Engagement.

2   The Project Manager shall act as the agent of the Client, and be responsible for the administration, management and communication co-ordination of the Project.

*Be sure to complete every clause which has an asterisk

111

3   The Project Manager shall:

(a) Communicate to the Consultants the requirements of the Client's Brief.

(b) Monitor the progress of design work, and the achievement of function by reference to the Client's Brief.

(c) Monitor and regulate programme and progress.

(d) Monitor and use his reasonable endeavours to co-ordinate the efforts of all Consultants, advisers, contractors and suppliers directly connected with the Project.

(e) Monitor the cost and financial rewards of the Project by reference to the Client's Brief.

4.1 The Project Manager shall not without the prior written consent of the Client give to the main or any other contractor or any supplier or any other person any instruction the necessary effect of which would be materially either to vary the Project or to increase the cost of or the time taken to complete the Project.

4.2 The Project Manager shall promptly inform the Client in writing of anything the likely effect of which the Project Manager believes would be materially either:

(a) to vary the Project; or

(b) to increase the cost of the Project or change its financial viability, quality or function; or

(c) to increase the time taken to complete the Project.

5   The Project Manager shall not be responsible for:

(a) Any forecasts of financial viability unless prepared by him.

(b) The Consultant's designs and technical co-ordination thereof.

(c) The advice or recommendations that may be provided by any Consultant or adviser appointed by the Client.

6.1 The Project Manager shall perform the Services with reasonable skill, care and diligence, but:

(a) no liability shall attach to the Project Manager in respect of the Services except such liability as ought to be covered by the professional indemnity insurance referred to in clause 12 of the Memorandum of Agreement;

(b) such liability shall be limited to the sum insured as specified in clause 12 of the Memorandum of Agreement.

6.2 No liability shall attach to the Project Manager either in contract or in tort or otherwise for loss, injury or damage sustained as a result of any defect in any material or the act, omission or insolvency of any person other than the Project Manager and the Project Manager shall not be liable to indemnify the Client in respect of any claim made against the Client for any such loss, injury or damage.

6.3 Clauses 6.1 (a) and (b) and 6.2 shall not be valid insofar as prohibited by statute.

7   The Memorandum of Agreement and the said Conditions of Engagement shall together constitute the Agreement between the Client and the Project Manager. Any variation thereof after the date of this Agreement shall only be by written consent of the parties.

* **8**   The date of commencement of this Agreement shall be ....

* **9**   The period of delay referred to in clause 5.6 of the Conditions of Engagement shall be

....

* 10 (a) The Client shall pay to the Project Manager the fee of .... for the services listed in Appendix A of the Conditions of Engagement.

   (b) Payment of the fee shall be made in accordance with Appendix C of the Conditions of Engagement.

* (c) The fee is based on completion of the project by

   .... 19..........

   (only completed if a lump sum fee is to be agreed).

* (d) The rate of interest referred to in clause 7.3 of the Conditions of Engagement is

   .... per cent.

* 11 The Project Manager will appoint .... as the principal person employed by the Project Manager who will undertake the direction and control of the Project Manager's duties and obligations under this Agreement (subject to the provisions of clause 3.3 of the Conditions of Engagement).

* 12 Professional indemnity insurance referred to in clause 15 of the Conditions of Engagement shall be effected for a sum of not less than

   £...

13 For the avoidance of doubt the obligations, liabilities and responsibilities of the Project Manager are as expressly stated herein. No additional obligations, liabilities or responsibilities whatsoever shall be implied.

14 No indulgence shown by either the Client or the Project Manager shall prevent the other subsequently insisting upon his rights and remedies under the Agreement.

AS WITNESS the hands of the parties the date first written above.

Duly Authorised Representative of the Client: ....

Witness: ....

Address: ....

....

Duly Authorised Representative of the Project Manager: ....

Witness: ....

Address: ....

....

OR if as a DEED:
Executed and delivered as a DEED by .... Limited/plc in the presence of:

Director ....

Secretary ....

Executed and delivered as a DEED by .... Limited/plc in the presence of:

Director ....

Secretary ....

SIGNED AND DELIVERED AS A DEED by the said

[insert full names here]

In the presence of:

Witness's Signature

Witness's Full Name

Address: ....

....

....

Occupation: ....

....

(Signature)

....

(Full Name)

SIGNED AND DELIVERED AS A DEED by the said

[insert full names here]

In the presence of:

Witness's Signature

Witness's Full Name

Address: ....

....

....

Occupation: ....

....

(Signature)

....

(Full Name)

114

CONDITIONS OF ENGAGEMENT FOR A PROFESSIONAL PROJECT MANAGER

■ General Conditions

1 Definitions

In this Agreement the following terms shall have the meanings hereby assigned:

- ■ 'The Client'—the person or company named in the Memorandum of Agreement
- ■ 'The Project Manager'—the person or company named in the Memorandum of Agreement
- ■ 'The Consultants'—any or all of the consultants appointed by the Client to undertake specialist design and other functions in connection with the Project
- ■ 'The Project'—the project with which the Client is proceeding and for which the services of the Project Manager have been engaged
- ■ 'The Brief'—the written brief provided by the Client to the Project Manager prior to the date of this Agreement to describe the objectives of time cost quality and function of the Project
- ■ 'The Services'—the services to be provided by the Project Manager and identified in this Agreement

2 Schedule of Services

2.1 The services to be provided by the Project Manager have been listed in Appendix A.

2.2 Additional services may from time to time be agreed between the parties. Any adjustment of payment to the Project Manager under clause 7.1 shall be agreed at the time.

3 Project Manager's Staff

3.1 The person named in clause 11 of the Memorandum of Agreement shall have full authority on behalf of the Project Manager.

3.2 The person named in clause 11 of the Memorandum of Agreement shall not be changed without the written consent of the Client. The replacement shall be approved by the Client in writing. Consent for the change, and approval of the replacement shall not be unreasonably withheld.

3.3 The Client may request the replacement of the person named in clause 11. The replacement shall be a member of the organization named as Project Manager. The Client shall approve the replacement in writing, and approval shall not be unreasonably withheld.

4 Collateral Warranty

4.1 Upon the written request of the Client, the Project Manager shall for a consideration or by deed collaterally warrant to any interested third party named by the Client that the Project Manager has performed or will perform the Services with reasonable skill, care and diligence in accordance with and subject to the provisions of this Agreement.

4.2 Such written request by the Client may be given at any time but no later than the end of the period of 2 years following the date of practical completion.

4.3 Nothing in clause 4.1 above shall give to such interested third party any right to direct or control the Project Manager in the performance of the Services.

5 Duration of Engagement

5.1 The appointment shall commence from the date stated in clause 8 of the Memorandum of Agreement.

5.2 The benefits and obligations of this Agreement may be assigned by either party but only with the prior written consent of the other.

5.3 The Client may terminate this appointment at any time by notice in writing. Upon termination the Client shall make a payment in accordance with clause 11.1.

5.4 The Client may postpone the Project and shall confirm such instruction in writing. Upon postponement the Client shall make a payment in accordance with clause 11.1.

5.5 If, following postponement, there is no resumption within six months, this appointment shall be automatically terminated.

5.6 The Project Manager may terminate this Agreement if the Project is delayed and he is prevented from carrying out his Services for a period of more than that stated in clause 9 of the Memorandum of Agreement.

5.7 Either party shall be entitled forthwith to terminate this Agreement by written notice to the other if:

5.7.1 That other party commits any breach of any of the provisions of this Agreement and, in the case of a breach capable of remedy, fails to remedy the same within 30 days after receipt of

INTRODUCTION

The purpose of the Handbook is to guide the Project Team in the performance of its duties, which are concerned with the design, construction and completion of a project to the required quality, within the parameters of the contract budget and to programme.

Its aim is to identify responsibilities and co-ordinate the various actions and procedures from other documents/data, already, or currently, or likely to be prepared, into one comprehensive and authoritative document, covering as a rule and depending on the nature/scope of project, the main elements and activities outlined in the following sections.

The Handbook is prepared by the Project Manager in consultation with the Project Team, where possible, at the beginning of the pre-construction stage and describes the general procedures to be adopted by the Client and the Team.

The Handbook is not a static document and it is anticipated that changes and amendments will be required in accordance with procedures, as later defined. Consequently, a loose-leaf format should be adopted to facilitate its updating by the Project Manager, who is the only person authorised to co-ordinate and implement revisions. Copies of the Handbook will be provided to each nominated member of the project team, as listed under section 'Parties to the Project' of the project concerned. (Appendix A, page 151)

PARTIES TO THE PROJECT

This will include:

- A list of all parties involved in the project, including those employed by the Client, as well as their contact details (addresses, phones, telex and facsimile numbers);

- The name of the Project Manager responsible for the project, together with details of his duties, responsibilities and authority (reference: Job Specification, Appendix 1.1, page 7);

- Details of other persons involved, complete with their duties, responsibilities and contacts;

- Organisation chart(s) indicating line and functional relationships, contractual and communication links, and schedules of the various stages/phases of the project.

THIRD PARTIES

This section will provide the names and contact details of all legal authority departments, public utilities, hospitals, doctors, police stations, fire brigade, trade

- Identification of items for pre-ordering and long delivery, preparation of tender documents, Client's approvals, and placement of orders and their confirmation.

- Monitoring production of drawings and specifications throughout the various stages of the project and their release to parties concerned.

- Arranging presentations to the Client at appropriate stages of design development and securing final approval to tender design;

- Reviewing, with the Professional Team, any necessary modifications to the design programme and Information Required Schedules (IRS) in the light of the appointed contractor(s)/sub-contractor(s)' requirements, and re-issuing revised programme/IRS.

- Preparing detailed and specialist designs and sub-contract packages, including bills of quantities.

- Making provision for adequate, safe and orderly storage of all drawings, specifications and schedules, including the setting up of an effective register/ records and retrieval system.

The Project Manager must ensure that the Client is fully aware that supplementary decisions must be obtained as the design stages progress and well within the specified (latest) dates, in order to avoid additional costs. Designs and specifications meeting the Client's brief and requirements, are appraised by the quantity surveyor for costs and are confirmed to be within the budgetary provisions.

VARIATIONS AND INSTRUCTIONS

The major areas subject to change will lie within the Client's brief, in the contract and in site instructions. Handling these changes will require a series of actions by the Project Manager as detailed below.

Client's Brief

The Project Manager will be responsible for:

- Administering all requests through the Change Order System (*see* Figure 5.2 and Appendix 5.1 for check list and specimen/form).

- Retaining all relevant documentation.

- A schedule of approved and pending orders which will be issued monthly.

- For ensuring that no changes are acted upon unless authorised by the above procedure.

Variations to the contract

- Giving consideration only to aspects requiring attention here include amendments and alterations to the programmes and drawings, as defined by the appropriate provisions of the applicable contract/agreement.

- Initial assessment by the Project Manager of any itemised request made by the Client (eg M&E and other services, finishes). The importance of time factors/limits is to be stressed.

- Consideration by Professional Team, including securing required statutory/ planning approvals and cost checking revised proposals. Confirmation to Client of action taken.

- Design process and preparation of instructions to contractor(s) involved.

- Cost agreement procedure for omissions and additions, ie estimates, disruptive costs, negotiations and time implications.

Site instructions

Such instructions should identify the parties involved and define the role of the Project Manager.

They must be issued in writing and confirmed in a similar manner by recipients.

Instructions for variations procedures can be categorised as:

— normal;

— special (eg concerned with immediate implementation as essential for safety, health and environmental protection aspects);

— extension of time required or predicted;

— additional payments involved or their estimate.

Instructions correctly approved will be contractually binding.

COST CONTROL AND REPORTING

The quantity surveyor has overall responsibility for cost monitoring and reporting with the assistance of and input from the Professional Team and contractor(s).

Action at the pre-construction stage involves:

- The preparation of preliminary comparison budget estimates.

- The agreement of the control budget with the Project Manager.

- Project budget being prepared in elemental form. The influence of grants is identified.

- The establishment of work packages and their cost budgets.

- Costing of change orders.

Other elements associated with work control are:

- Assessment of cost implications for all designs, including cost comparison of alternative design solution.

- Value analysis procedures, including cost-in-use.

- Comparison of alternative forms of construction using data on their methodology and costs.

- Comparison of cost budgets and tenderers' prices at sub-contract tender assessment.

- Tenders which are outside the budget and which require an input from the Project Manager on such matters as:

  — alteration of specifications to reduce costs;

  — acceptance of tender figure and accommodating increased cost from contingency. Alternatively, the Client may accept the increase and seek savings from other areas;

  — possible re-tendering by alternative contractors.

- Production of monthly cost reports including:

  — variations since last report, incorporating reasons for costs increase/decrease;

  — current projected total cost for the project;

  — cash flow for the project: (i) forecast of expenditure; (ii) actual cash flow as programme monitoring device indicating potential overspending and any areas of delay or likely problems.

The report should be agreed with and issued to the Project Manager who will

— give advice and initiate action on any problems that are identified;

— arrange distribution of copies, according to a predetermined list.

PLANNING, PROGRAMMES AND PROGRESS REPORTING

Planning is a key area and can have a significant effect on the outcome of a project. The associated activities include:

- Determining the composition and duties of planning support team and the appropriate techniques to be used (eg bar charts, networks).

- Preparation of the final outline Project Master Programme and seeking the Client's acceptance.

- Co-ordination of Design Team, contractors and Client's activities programme.

- Production of outline pre and construction programmes indicating likely project duration and the basis for determining the procurement programme.

- Production of an outline procurement programme, including the latest date for placement of orders (materials, equipment, contractors) and design release dates.

- Modifications, if necessary, to the outline construction programme due to constraints.

- Production of the outline design programme including:

  — the sequence and timing for preparation of the design information;

  — a Client's decisions schedule;

  — necessary modifications due to external limitations.

- Preparation of the Project Master Programme.

- Start up and operation of a detailed design involving:

  — a short term programme for pre-construction stage;

  — monthly reviews;

- production of a detailed design programme in consultation with, and incorporating, design elements from the Professional Team members concerned;

- agreement by Client, Professional Team and Project Manager.

- Preparation of a drawing control schedule which should be confirmed by the Professional Team and Project Manager. This will need to be formally accepted by the Client, who will also indicate at which points his decision will be required.

- Reviewing the outline procurement programme and its translation into one which is detailed.

- Production of programmes for bills of quantities procurement and tender documentation control.

- Expansion of outline construction programme into one which is detailed.

- Identification of construction phases for tender documentation.

- Preparation of programmes for:

  - enabling works;

  - fitting out (if part of the project);

  - completion and handover;

  - occupation/migration (if part of the project).

- Progress monitoring and reporting procedures should be on a monthly basis and agreed following consultation with members of Professional Team and contractor(s). Reports will need to be supplied to the Client/Project Manager.

- Monitoring progress against Project Master Programmes on a monthly basis, with the Client/Project Manager being informed.

MEETINGS

Meetings are required to maintain effective communications between the Project Manager, Project Team and other parties concerned, eg those responsible for industrial relations and emergencies, as well as the Client.

The frequency and location of meetings and those taking part will be the responsibility of the Project Manager. Meetings held too frequently can lead to a waste of time whereas communications can suffer where meetings are infrequent.

Procedures

- Agenda – issued in advance, stating action/submissions required.

- Minutes and circulation list (time limits involved). (Examples of Agenda and Minutes – *see* Appendix 4.1, page 62.)

- Contractor(s) should be invited to meetings between the Professional Team and sub-contractor(s) and architects for meetings with consultants and specialist advisers.

- Written confirmation and acknowledgement of instructions given at meetings (time limit involved).

- Reports/materials tabled at meetings to be sent in advance to Chairman.

Typical meetings and their objectives

'Steering Group/Team'

— to consider project brief, design concepts, capital budget and programme(s);

— to approve changes to project brief;

— to review project strategies and overall progress towards achieving Client's goals;

— to approve appointments for consultants and contractor(s).

'Project Management Team'

— to agree cost plan and report on actual expenditure against agreed plan;

— to review tender lists, tenders received and decide on awarding work;

— to report on progress on design and construction programmes;

— to review and make recommendations for proposed changes to design and costs including Client changes. Approve relevant modifications to project programme(s).

'Design Team' — to review, report on and implement all matters related to design and cost;

— to determine/review Client decisions;

— to prepare information/report/advice to 'Project Management Team' on (i) appointment of sub/specialist contractors; (ii) proposed design and/or cost changes;

— to review receipt, co-ordination and processing of sub-contractors' design information;

— to ensure overall co-ordination of design and design information.

'Finance Group/Team'

— to review, monitor and report financial, contractual and procurement aspects to appropriate parties;

— to prepare a project cost plan for approval by Client;

— to prepare and review regular cost reports and cash flows, including forecasts of additional expenditure;

— to review taxation matters;

— to monitor the preparation and issue of all tender and contract documentation;

— to review cost implications of proposed Client and Design Team changes.

'Project Team' (Programme/Progress meeting)

— to provide effective communication between teams responsible for the various phases of the project;

— to monitor progress and report on developments, proposed changes and programme(s) implications;

— to review progress against programme(s) for each stage/section of the project/works and identify any problems;

— to review procurement status;

— to review status of information for construction and contractor(s)' sub-contractors' requests for information.

'Project Team' (site meeting)

Main contractor report tabled monthly to include details on:

— quality control;

— progress;

— welfare (health, safety, canteen, industrial relations);

— sub-contractors;

— design and procurement;

— information required;

— site security;

— drawing registers.

Reports/reviews (including matters arising from previous meetings):

— architect;

— building services;

— facilities management;

— information technology;

— quantity surveyor.

Statutory undertakings and utilities:

— telephones;

— gas;

— water;

— electricity;

— drainage.

Approvals and consents:

planning;

— Building Regulations;

— Local Authority Engineer;

— Public Health Department;

— others.

Information:

— issued by design team (AIs issued and architect's tender activity summary);

— required from Design Team;

— required from contractor.

SELECTION AND APPOINTMENT OF CONTRACTORS

The Project Manager, as the Client's representative, has the responsibility, with the support of the Professional Team, for the selection and appointment of:

— contractor(s), eg main, management, design and build;

— contractors, eg specialist, works, trade.

The various processes associated with this activity are summarised in the following.

Composition of selection panel appointments relevant to the nature and scope of tender to be awarded. Nomination of a co-ordinator (contact) for all matters concerned with the tender.

Establishment of selection/appointment procedures for each stage (*see* Appendix 2.3 for Assessment Sheet, page 19, and Appendices B1–B13 for checklists and other relevant material, pages 152–65).

Pre-tender

— assessment of essential criteria/expertise required for a specific tender;

— preparation of long (provisional) list, embracing known and prospective tenderers;

— checks against database available to Project Manager, especially financial viability and quality of past and current work. Possible use of telephone questionnaire to obtain additional data;

— potential tenderers invited to complete/submit selection questionnaire. Short list finalised accordingly;

Arrangements for pre-qualification interview, including prior issue of following documentation relevant to the project to the prospective tenderer with interview agenda, outline of special requirements and expected attendees;

— general scope of contract works and summary of conditions;

— preliminary drawings and specifications;

— summary of Project Master and construction programmes;

— pricing schedule;

— safety, health and environmental protection statement;

— labour relations statement;

— quality management outline.

Tender and reserve lists finalised.

Tendering process

- Selected tenderers confirm willingness to submit bona fide tender. Reserve list is employed in the event of any withdrawals and selection made in accordance with placement order.

- Tender documents issued and consideration given by both parties to whether mid-tender interview is required or would be beneficial.

- Interview arranged and agenda issued.

Returned tenders' review

- Evaluation of received tenders.

- Arrangements for post-tender interview and prior issue of agenda.

- Final evaluation and report.

- Pre-order check and approval to place order.

SAFETY, HEALTH AND ENVIRONMENTAL PROTECTION

It is the responsibility of the main contractor to formulate policy for the site, to be adhered to by all contractors, and reach agreement on relevant specific standards and performance targets.

These are supplementary to any municipal, local or governmental regulations and requirements and are within the letter and spirit of the Health and Safety at Work Act.

Contractors are required, as part of their tender submission, to provide copies of their safety policy statement which outlines safe working methods.

Other matters which come within the remit of the main contractor are:

- The establishment and enforcement, within the contractual provisions, of rules, regulations and practices to prevent accidents, incidents or events resulting in injury or fatality to any person on the site, or damage or destruction to site's or neighbouring owners'/occupiers' property, equipment and materials.

- Arranging First Aid facilities, warning signals and possible evacuation, as well as the display of relevant notices, posters and instructions.

- Instituting procedures for:

  — regular inspections and spot checks;

  — reporting to the Project Manager (with copies to Professional Team members concerned) on any non-compliance and the corrective or preventive action taken;

  — hazardous situations necessitating work stoppage and in extreme cases, closedown of the site.

QUALITY ASSURANCE (QA) – OUTLINE

(Applicable only if QA is operated as part of contractual provisions.)

Critical to the operation of a QA scheme is for the Client to have an understanding of the scheme, its application and limits of assurance, and the need for defects insurance.

Procedures and controls will need to be established to ascertain compliance with design and specifications and to confirm that standards of workmanship and materials quality have been attained.

The Professional Team will review, with the Project Manager, details of their quality control.

The contractor(s)' quality plan indicates how the quality process is to be managed, including control arrangements for sub-contractor(s).

Responsibility for monitoring site operation of QA administration and control procedures for the relevant documents will need to be established.

DISPUTES

Procedures for all parties involved in the project in the event of disagreement and disputes are to be specified in accordance with the contractual conditions/provisions of the project concerned.

REPORTING

The following are examples of the reports which might be prepared:

Sign off documents – Frequency: progressively during stages of brief, strategy, schematic design and (if in use) 'milestone schedule'. Distribution List.

Project Manager's progress report

To be issued monthly and include details of:

- Project status:

  — updated capital budget;

  — accommodation schedule;

  — authorised Change Orders during the month;

  — other relevant matters.

- Operational brief.

- Design development status.

- Cost plan status and summary of financial report.

- Programme and progress – design.

                                 – construction.

- Change Orders.

- Client decisions and information requirements.

- Legal and estates.

- Facilities management.

- Fitting out and occupation/(migration) planning.

- Risks and uncertainties.

- Update of anticipated final completion date.

- Distribution list.

Professional Team report

Issued monthly and including input from consultants and containing details on:

- Design development status.

- Status of tender documents.

- Information produced during the month.

- Change Orders – design progress.

- Information requirement/requests status.

- Status of contractor(s)/sub-contractor's drawings/submittals.

- Quality control.

- Distribution list.

Financial Control (QS) report

Issued monthly and including:

- Reconciliation capital sanction/capital budget.

- Updated cost plan and anticipated final cost projection.

- Authorised Change Orders – effects.

- Pending Change Orders – implications.

- Contingency sum.

- Cashflow.

- VAT.

- Distribution list.

Daily/Weekly Diary

Prepared by each senior member of the Project Team and filed in own separate loose leaf binder for quick reference and convenient follow-up. Diaries are made accessible to the Project Manager and contain the following typical items:

— summary of forward and ad hoc meetings and persons attending;

— summary of critical telephone conversations/messages;

— documents received or issued;

— problems, comments or special situations and their resolution;

— programme status (eg work packages progress or delays);

— critical events and work observations;

— critical instructions given or required;

— requests for decisions or actions to be taken;

— approximate time of day for each entry;

— distribution list.

CONSTRUCTION STAGE

The Project Manager will introduce checks and monitoring procedures for:

- All drawings, specifications and relevant certificates issued to contractors.

- Actioning the Professional Team's instructions, lists, schedules and valuations.

- The following aspects prior to commencement:

  — recording existing site conditions, including adjacent properties;

  — ensuring that all relevant contracts are in place and that all applicable conditions have been met;

  — confirming that all risk insurance for site and adjacent properties is in force;

  — ensuring that all site facilities are to the required standard, including provisions for safety, health and environmental protection.

- Construction work, including:

  — reviewing contractor's preliminary programme against Master Programme and agreeing adjustments;

  — ensuring checks by main contractor on sub-contractor(s) programmes;

  — checking and monitoring all contractor's adequacy of planned and actual resources to achieve the programme;

  — approvals for sub-letting in accordance with contractual provisions;

  — reporting on and adjusting programmes as appropriate;

  — checks for early identification of actual or potential problems (seeking Client's agreement to solutions of significant problems).

- Controls for variations and claims (*see* page 128).

- Controls for the preparation and issue of Change Orders (*see* Figure 5.2, page 66 and Appendix 5.1, page 69).

- Processing the following applications for Client's action:

  — interim payments from Professional Team members and contractors;

  — final accounts from Professional Team members;

  — final accounts from contractors, subject to receipt of relevant certification;

  — payment of other invoices.

- Making contact and keeping informed the various authorities concerned to facilitate final approvals.

  The Professional team members will:

- Supervise and inspect works in accordance with contractual provisions/conditions and participate in and contribute to:

  — the monitoring and adjustment of the Master Programme;

  — controls for variations and claims;

  — identification and solutions of actual or potential problems;

  — sub-letting approvals;

  — preparation of change orders.

FITTING OUT, OUTSTANDING WORKS AND RECTIFICATION

This stage can either be a part of the overall project, or be a separate project on its own, eg for a 'shell and core' contract. In the latter case the Project Manager also acts as Client's Representative with full executive powers. The decision as to which option to choose is made at the strategy stage. The following summarise the various stages:

Rectification of building/construction outstanding works

- Inspecting facility to confirm availability.

- Preparation of schedule of outstanding works for Client.

- Obtaining Practical Completion Certificate for the facility.

- Achieving acceptance of the outstanding works list by the Client and agreeing programme for completion.

- Confirmation of acceptance of completion programme by fitting out contractor.

- Monitoring completion of outstanding works programme and issue of fitting out Practical Completion Certificate.

Fitting out

- The Project Manager assists and advises Client with the following:

  — preparation of heads of agreements for a lease and lease;

  — preparation of lease marketing material and implementation of marketing or promotional campaign;

  — works carried out under construction contract, or executed by other methods and selection of suitable contractor;

  — preparation of drawings, specifications and relevant contracts.

- Tenant liaison will involve the provision of information enabling tenant(s) to formulate fitting out proposals and securing the Client's approval.

- Contractor liaison has the following features:

  — checking that the contractor has necessary insurance and local authority approval to start work;

  — checking current status of design and specifications and ensuring their issue to the contractor;

  — reviewing and agreeing scope of work, programmes and co-ordination, as well as applicable regulations and controls, including Client's special conditions, eg access and interface with other working parties;

  — monitoring work and progress against specifications and programme and ensuring compliance with all Client's requirements;

  — obtaining fitting out certificates.

- Financial considerations:

  — checking Client's payments to contractors;

  — monitoring and recording any contra charges;

  — agreeing contra charges and balancing payments with Client.

COMMISSIONING, COMPLETION AND HANDOVER

Inspecting, testing and mock-ups

The architect, the other members of the Professional Team concerned and the Project Manager collaborate in formulating recommendations to the Client for establishing:

- On and off site inspection of the works for compliance with specifications, and the testing of materials and workmanship.

- Performance testing and criteria to be adopted.

- Schedules and the regular updating of samples and mock-ups required, and monitoring progress of approvals. Copies of schedules included in the relevant monthly reports.

Members of the Professional Team have responsibility for:

- Regular inspection of works for which they have design responsibility and the issue of reports on progress, compliance with specifications, and any corrective action to be taken by contractor(s).

- Inspection of work at Practical Completion, production of the Outstanding Works Schedule and signing off, hence certifying completion, subject to outstanding work carried out.

- Final inspection and check at the end of a contract Defects Liability Period, to ensure rectification of all defects, that any omissions are made good and that all necessary repairs are carried out. The architect issues the Certificate of Completion on receipt of a satisfactory report. The Final Certificate is issued following agreement of final account between the quantity surveyor and contractor.

Completion

Agreements and procedures are needed for partial possession and phased (sectional) completion.

- Access, inspections, defects, continuation of other works and/or operation of any plant/services installation, material obstructions or restrictions.

- Certification on and possession at each phase. Responsibility for insurance.

Agreements and procedures associated with practical completion are:

- User's/tenant's responsibility for whole of the insurance.

- Provision, within a specified time limit, of complete sets of as-built and installed drawings, M&E and other relevant installations/services data, as well as all operating manuals and commissioning reports.

- Storage of equipment/materials except those required for making good defects.

- Access for completion of minor construction works, rectification of defects, testing of services, verification of user(s) works and other welfare and general facilities.

Commissioning

Engineering services commissioning is part of the construction stage. It is the main contractor's responsibility which is delegated to the services sub-contractors. Action at the pre- and post-contract stages is indicated in the following:

Pre-contract
- Ensuring the Client recognises engineering services commissioning as a distinct phase of the construction process.

- Ensuring the Professional Team identifies all services to be commissioned and defining responsibility split for commissioning between contractor/manufacturer/Client.

- Identifying statutory and insurance approvals required and planning to meet requirements and obtain approvals.

- Co-ordinating the Professional Team and Client's involvement in commissioning to ensure conformity with the contract arrangements.

- Arranging single point responsibility for control and the Client's role in the commissioning of services.

- Ensuring contract documents make provision for services commissioning.

Post-contract
- Ensuring relevant integration within construction programmes.

- Monitoring and reporting progress and arranging corrective action.

- Ensuring provision and proper maintenance of records, test results, certificates, checklists, software and drawings.

- Arranging for or advising on maintenance staff training.

Client commissioning involves:

- Arranging the appointment of the Commissioning Team in liaison with the Client and establishing objectives (time, cost, quality) and responsibilities.

- The preparation of a comprehensive commissioning and equipment programme.

- Arranging access to the works for Commissioning Team and Client personnel during construction – including observation of engineering services commissioning.

- Ensuring co-ordination and liaison with the construction processes and Professional Team.

- Preparing new work practices manuals, staff training and recruitment of additional staff (eg 'Aftercare Engineer' to support the Client during the initial period of occupancy).

- Deciding format of commissioning records.

- Renting equipment to meet short term demands.

- Deciding quality standards.

- Monitoring and controlling commissioning progress and reporting to Client.

- Reviewing operation of building (6, 9, 12 months) – improvements, defects, corrections and related feedback.

  Note: Examples of checklists and documentation are given in Appendices C, D and E, pages 166–9.

Handover

The responsibilities of the Project Manager are to:

- Ensure that handover only takes place when all statutory inspections and approvals have been satisfactorily completed, and that all outstanding works and defects are resolved before expiry of the defects liability period.

- Agree a countdown programme with the Project Team (examples of Handover Inspections and Certificates Checklists are given in Appendix F, page 170).

- Confirm responsibilities for all inspections and certificates.

- Monitor and control handover countdown against the programme.

- Set up a pre-handover Control Procedure if the Client has access to the building before handover.

- Establish procedures for dealing with contractors who fail to carry out outstanding works or correct defects and discuss with the Professional Team the possibility of implementing any contra-charging measures available under the contract. Agree and set up a procedure for contra-charging.

- Set up appropriate procedures to monitor and control any post-handover works which do not form part of the main contract.

- Set up an End of Defects Liability Period procedure and programme. Agree to implement this procedure.

- Monitor and control outstanding post-completion work and resolution of defects against the above procedures, to completion of the project.

OCCUPATION (MIGRATION)

(Examples of checklists given at Appendix 8.1.)

This stage can either be a part of the overall project, or be a separate project on its own. A decision to this effect is made at the strategy stage.

Structure for implementation

Individuals and groups are appointed in order to achieve the necessary direction and consultations, eg:

- Project Executive (Client/Occupier/Tenant)

- Occupation Co-ordinator (Project Manager)

- Occupation Steering Group

  — chairman, co-ordinator and functional representatives.

  — concerned with overall direction for:
  construction programme;
  technology;
  space planning;
  facilities for removal;
  user representation;
  costs and budget outline.

- Senior Representative meeting

  — chairman (functional representative on Steering Group), co-ordinator and senior representatives of majority of employees

  — concerned with consultations on:
  space planning;
  corporate communications;
  construction programme problems;
  technology.

- Local representatives' Groups

  — chaired by Manager/Supervisor of own group;

  — concerned with consultation at locations and/or departmental levels in order to ensure procedures for regular communications.

Scope and objectives (Regularly reviewed.)

- Identification who is to move (Project Executive).

- Agreement on placement of people in new location(s) (Steering Group).

- Decision on organisation of move (Steering Group);

  — all at once;

  — several moves;

  — gradual flow.

- Reviewing time constraints (Steering Group);

  — construction;

  — commercial;

  — holidays.

- Identification of risk areas, eg

  — construction delays and move flexibility;

  — organisational changes;

  — access problems;

  — information technology requirements;

  — furniture deliveries and refurbishment;

  — retrofit requirements.

Methodology (Steering Group)

- Listing special activities needed to complete the move, eg

  — additional building work;

  — communications during move;

- provision of necessary services and move support;

- corporate communications;

- removal administration;

- furniture procurement;

- removal responsibility in each location/department;

- financial controls;

- access planning.

- Preparation of task list for each special activity, confirmation of person responsible, and setting the schedule of project meetings;

- Production of outline and subsequently detailed programme.

Organisation and Control

- Steering Group establishes 'Move Group' to oversee the physical move.

- Production of 'count down' programme (Move Group).

- Identification of external resources needed (Move Group), eg:

- special management skills;

- one-off support tasks;

- duplication of functions during move.

- Reporting to Client external support needs and costs (Steering Group).

- Preparation of monitoring and regularly review actual budget (Steering Group) eg:

- dual occupancy;

- special facilities;

- additional engineering and technology needs;

- planning and co-ordinating process;

- inflation;

- external resources;

- non-recoverable VAT;

- contingencies.

APPENDIX A   HANDBOOK UPDATE FORM

Issue No: ....
Date: ....

Please find attached revised/additional sheets. Please insert in your copy of the handbook and remove redundant sheets.

Section	Page(s)/ Ref	Previous Issues				Remarks
		No 1 dated	No 2 dated	No 3 dated	No 4 dated	

Distribution:

Project Manager's Signature ....

APPENDIX B SELECTION AND APPOINTMENT OF CONTRACTORS:

B1 PRE-TENDER PROCESS

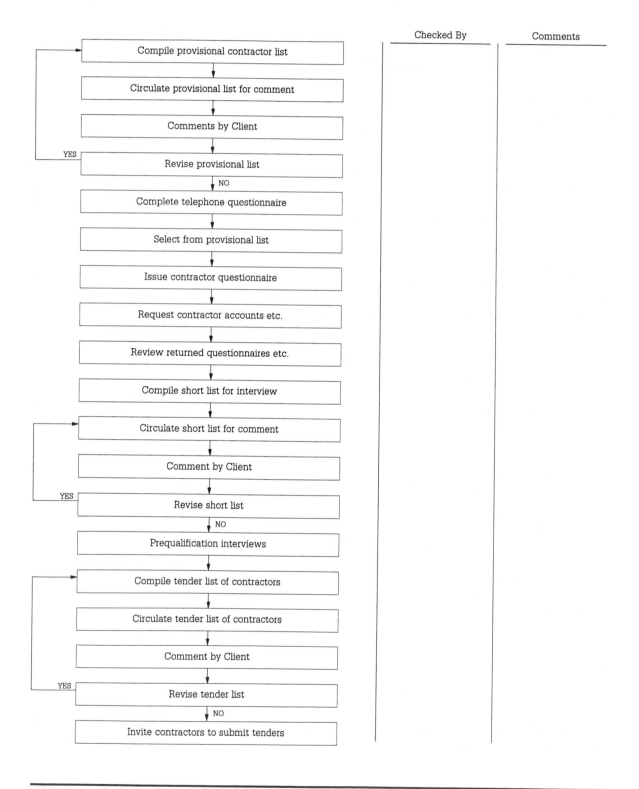

APPENDIX B SELECTION AND APPOINTMENT OF CONTRACTORS:

B2 INITIAL (OR TELEPHONE) QUESTIONNAIRE

'PROJECT MANAGEMENT LTD'	FORM Q1
REF. NUMBER: CONTRACT TITLE:	

Item No.	Question	Response
1.0	Turnover of company?	
2.0	What is the value of contracts secured to date?	
3.0	What is the largest current contract?	
4.0	Is the contractor willing to submit a tender?	
5.0	Is the contractor willing to work with all team members?	
6.0	Is the contract period acceptable?	
7.0	If not, how long to complete works?	
8.0	Is the anticipated tender period acceptable?	
9.0	If not, how long to tender?	
10.0	What are the mobilisation periods:- (a) completion of drawings? (b) fabrication? (c) start on site from order?	
11.0	Is the labour used direct, self employed or subcontract?	
12.0	What element of the contract will be sub-let?	

Comments:
Signature and date _____

APPENDIX B   SELECTION AND APPOINTMENT OF CONTRACTORS:

B3   SELECTION QUESTIONNAIRE

1 Name of company:	
2 Address:	
3 Telephone no.:	Facsimile no.:
4 Nature of business:	

5 Indicate whether:
  (a) manufacturer
  (b) supplier
  (c) subcontractor
  (d) main contractor
  (e) design and build contractor
  (f) management contractor	

6 Indicate whether:
  (a) sole trader
  (b) partnership
  (c) private
  (d) public	

7 Company registration number:	
8 Year of registration:	
9 Bank and branch:	
10 VAT registration number:	
11 Tax exemption certificate number: date of expiry:	
12 State annual turnover of current and previous four years:	
13 State value of future secured work:	
14 State maximum and minimum value of works undertaken:	
15 Are you registered under BS 5750?	
16 State previous projects undertaken with 'P.M. LTD'	
17 Are you prepared to sign a design warranty?	
18 Are you prepared to provide a performance bond?	
19 Are you prepared to provide a parent company guarantee?	
20 Do you operate a holiday with pay scheme?	
21 State when stamps last purchased:	

APPENDIX B3 continued

22 Do you contribute to the C. I. T. B.?	
23 Are you registered under N. W. R. 26?	
24 Do you have a safety policy?	
25 Employers liability insurance: insuror: policy no.: expiry date: limit of indemnity:	
26 Third party insurance: insurer: policy no.: expiry date: limit of indemnity:	
27 Which elements do you sublet?	
28 List of projects of similar size and complexity: Project 1.: Address: Architect: Contact: Contractor: Contact: Value: Year completed: Project 2.: Address: Architect: Contact: Contractor: Contact: Value: Year completed: Project 3.: Address: Architect: Contact: Contractor: Contact: Value: Year completed:	telephone no.: telephone no.: telephone no.: telephone no.: telephone no.: telephone no.:

APPENDIX B SELECTION AND APPOINTMENT OF CONTRACTORS:

B4 PRE QUALIFICATION INTERVIEW AGENDA

'PROJECT MANAGEMENT LTD'	FORM A1
REF. NUMBER: CONTRACT TITLE:	

1.0	INTRODUCTION
1.1	Purpose of meeting
1.2	Introduction to those present
2.0	DESCRIPTION OF OVERALL PROJECT AND PROGRAMME
2.1	General description of the project
2.2	Master programme in summary
2.3	General description of contract
3.0	EXPLANATION OF CONTRACT TERMS AND CONDITIONS
3.1	Outline and scope of contract
3.2	Responsibilities of the contractor
3.3	Outline of contract conditions including any significant amendments
3.4	Programme
3.5	Specification
3.6	Drawings
3.7	Preliminaries
3.8	Budget prices
4.0	PROJECT ORGANISATION
4.1	Site administration and project team
4.2	Setting out and dimensional control
4.3	Materials handling and control
4.4	Site establishment
4.5	Contractor supervision and on-site representative
4.6	Site safety and labour relations
4.7	Quality management
5.0	TENDERING
5.1	Period of tendering
5.2	Mid-tender interview
5.3	Tender return date, address and contact name
6.0	ACTIONS REQUIRED
6.1	Summary of actions and date deadlines

APPENDIX B SELECTION AND APPOINTMENT OF CONTRACTORS:

B5 TENDERING PROCESS CHECKLIST

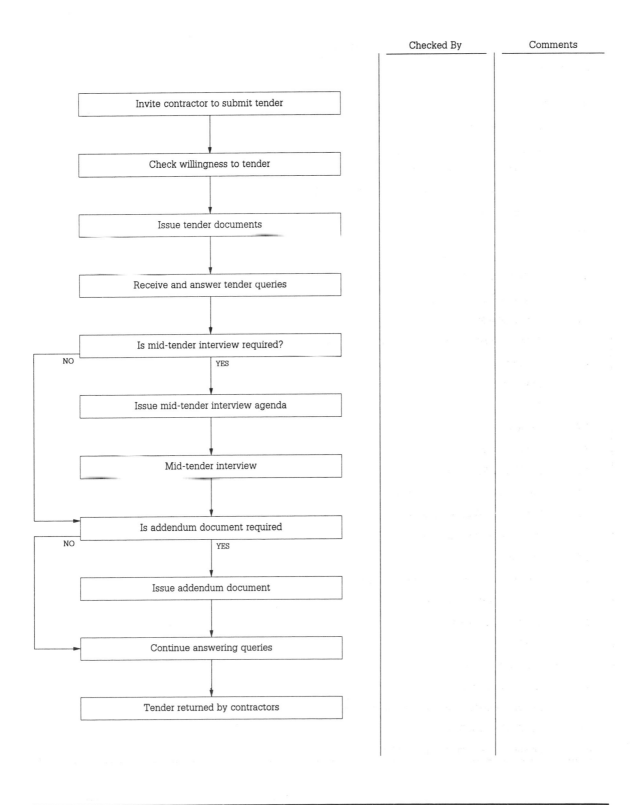

APPENDIX B SELECTION AND APPOINTMENT OF CONTRACTORS:

B6 TENDER DOCUMENT CHECK LIST

'PROJECT MANAGEMENT LTD'	FORM C1
REF. NUMBER:	
CONTRACT TITLE:	

☐ Invitation to tender

☐ Introduction and scope of contract

☐ Instructions to tenderers

☐ Form of tender

☐ General preliminaries

☐ Particular preliminaries

☐ Form of contract and amendments

☐ Contract programme

☐ Method statement

☐ Quality management

☐ Project safety

☐ Project labour relations

☐ Specification

☐ List of drawings

☐ Bill of quantities or pricing schedule

☐ General summary

☐ Declaration of non-collusion

☐ Performance bond

☐ Warranty

☐ Soils report

☐ Contamination reports

Other documents (please list below)

☐

☐

☐

☐

☐

☐

APPENDIX B SELECTION AND APPOINTMENT OF CONTRACTORS:

B7 MID-TENDER INTERVIEW AGENDA

'PROJECT MANAGEMENT LTD'	FORM A2
REF. NUMBER: CONTRACT TITLE:	

1.0	INTRODUCTION
1.1	Purpose of meeting
1.2	Introduction of those present
2.0	CONFIRMATION OF ADDENDA, LETTERS ISSUED
3.0	RESPONSES TO EXISTING QUERIES
3.1	Contractor
3.2	Architect
3.3	Civil and structural engineer
3.4	Mechanical and electrical engineer
3.5	Other consultants
3.6	Quantity surveyors
3.7	Project Manager
4.0	OTHER ADDITIONAL INFORMATION
4.1	Contractor
4.2	Architect
4.3	Civil and structural engineer
4.4	Mechanical and electrical engineer
4.5	Other consultants
4.6	Quantity surveyors
4.7	Project Manager
5.0	CONTRACTOR'S QUERIES
6.0	CONFIRMATION OF TENDER ARRANGEMENTS
6.1	Date
6.2	Time
6.3	Address
7.0	ANY OTHER BUSINESS

APPENDIX B SELECTION AND APPOINTMENT OF CONTRACTORS:

B8 RETURNED TENDER REVIEW PROCESS

APPENDIX B SELECTION AND APPOINTMENT OF CONTRACTORS:

B9 RETURNED TENDER BIDS RECORD SHEET

'PROJECT MANAGEMENT LTD'			FORM R1
REF. NUMBER:			
CONTRACT TITLE:			
ALLOCATED BUDGET		PROGRAMME PERIOD	
No.	CONTRACTOR, QUALIFICATIONS ETC	PROG.	BID SUM
1.			
2.			
3.			
4.			
5.			
6.			
7.			
8.			

Signed by the undersigned as a true record of duly and properly received tender bids for_____
on this day _____ (day) _____ (month) _____ in the year _____.

Signed:
Company:
Signed:
Company:
Signed:
Company:
Signed:
Company:

APPENDIX B SELECTION AND APPOINTMENT OF CONTRACTORS:

B10 POST TENDER INTERVIEW AGENDA

'PROJECT MANAGEMENT LTD'	FORM A3
REF. NUMBER: CONTRACT TITLE:	

1.0	INTRODUCTION
1.1	Introduction to those present
1.2	Purpose of meeting
2.0	CONFIRMATION OF CONTRACT SCOPE AND RESPONSIBILITIES
3.0	DETAILED BID DISCUSSIONS
3.1	Contractual
3.2	Cost
3.3	Programme
3.4	Method
3.5	Technical matters
3.6	Staffing, labour and plant matters
3.7	Labour relations matters
3.8	Site safety matters
3.7	Quality management
4.0	CONTRACTOR QUERIES
5.0	ACTION AND RESPONSES
5.1	Agreement of action items
5.2	Agreement of deadline dates for resolution of action items

APPENDIX B SELECTION AND APPOINTMENT OF CONTRACTORS:

B11 FINAL TENDER EVALUATION REPORT

'PROJECT MANAGEMENT LTD'	FORM R2
REF. NUMBER: CONTRACT TITLE:	

1.0   Summary of final tender bids following post tender interviews

2.0   Cost appraisal

3.0   Programme appraisal

4.0   Method statement appraisal

5.0   Technical appraisal

6.0   Contractual appraisal

7.0   Quality management appraisal

8.0   Safety appraisal

9.0   Labour relations appraisal

10.0   Recommendation to place contract

Appendices

1 Completed tender bid of recommended tenderer
2 Addenda and other information issues during tendering
3 Mid tender interview meeting minutes
4 Query lists and responses
5 Post tender meeting minutes
6 Any other letters etc. since tender issue
7 Summary of contract buy and any other items to be bought

APPENDIX B SELECTION AND APPOINTMENT OF CONTRACTORS:

B12 APPROVAL TO PLACE CONTRACT ORDER

'PROJECT MANAGEMENT LTD'	FORM O1

REF. NUMBER:

CONTRACT TITLE:

In accordance with Clause _____ of the _____

_____ (Contract Form)

We, _____

do not have any objection to the placing of a contract with_____

for_____

all in accordance with the tender recommendation report submitted to us on the _____ (date).

In submitting the tender recommendation report the Professional Team is fully satisfied that the contractor has complied in full with the tender documents and is fully capable of carrying out the contract works.

Signed by: _____

Signed by: _____

Signed by: _____

APPENDIX B SELECTION AND APPOINTMENT OF CONTRACTORS:

B13 FINAL GENERAL CHECK LIST

'PROJECT MANAGEMENT LTD'	FORM C3
REF. NUMBER: CONTRACT TITLE:	

Check once again that the following were carried out:

☐   Long list

☐   Telephone selection questionnaires

☐   Contractor selection questionnaires, company accounts, references and any
reports of visits to offices, factories and contracts

☐   Short list

☐   Pre-qualification interview minutes

☐   Tender list

☐   Substitute tender list

☐   Tender documents and check list

☐   Tender query lists, addendum, letters prior to mid-tender interviews

☐   Mid-tender interview minutes

☐   Tender query lists, addendum, letters etc. post mid-tender interviews

☐   Returned tender summary form and returned tender documents

☐   Interim tender analysis and recommendations report

☐   Post-tender query lists to contractors

☐   Post-tender interview minutes

☐   Post-tender addendum, letters etc

☐   Final tender analysis and recommendations report

☐   Contractor acceptability final check

☐   Approval to place contract order

APPENDIX C CLIENT COMMISSIONING CHECKLIST

Brief

Ensure roles and responsibilities for commissioning team are understood.

Budget

Programme

Based upon a clear understanding and agreement of the Client's objectives.

Commissioning action checklist

Investigate and identify commissioning requirements.
Management control document.

Appointments

Commissioning Team.
Operating and maintenance personnel.
'Aftercare Engineer'.
Job descriptions, timescales and outputs must be documented and agreed.

Client operating procedures

Work practice standards.
Health and safety at work requirements.

Training of staff

Services.
Security.
Maintenance.
Procedures.
Equipment.

Client equipment (including equipment rented for commissioning)

Programme.
Selection.
Approval.
Delivery.
Installation.

Building services and equipment

Define/check standards required in tender specification.
Testing.
Balancing ⎫
Adjusting ⎬ detail format of records
Fine tuning ⎭
Marking and labelling, including preparation of record drawings.
Handover of spares ⎫ must be compatible with any planned maintenance or
Handover of tools ⎬ equipment standardisation policies.

APPENDIX C continued

Maintenance

Acceptance by Client's maintenance section from the Client's construction and commissioning team.
Arrangements.
Procedures.
Contracts.

Security

Alarm systems.
Telephone link.
Staff routes.
Access (including card access).
Fire routes.
Bank cash dispensers.

Communications

Telephones.
Radios.
Paging.
Public address system.
Easy to read plan of building.
Data links.

Signs and graphics

Code of practice for the industry.
Statutory notices – H&S, fire, Factories Act, unions.

Initiation of operations

Final cleaning.
Maintenance procedures (including manufacturers' specialist maintenance).
Cleaning and refuse collection.
Insurance required by date and extent of cover will vary with the form of contract.
Access and security (including staff identity cards).
Safety.
Meter readings or commencement of accounts for gas, water, electricity, telephone and fuel oil.
Equipping.
Staff 'decanting'.
Publicity.
Opening arrangements.

Review operation of facility

+ 6, 9, 12 months (including energy costs).
Improvements and system fine tuning.
Defects reporting and correction verification procedures.
Latent defects.

Feedback

Channelled through 'Aftercare Engineer', if appointed.

APPENDIX D ENGINEERING SERVICES COMMISSIONING CHECKLIST

Engineering services to be covered

Routinely:
Water supply and sanitation.
Heating/cooling systems (boilers, calorifiers, chillers).
Ventilation systems.
Air conditioning.
Electrical (generators, switchboards, others).
Mechanical (pumps, motors, others).
Fire detection and protection systems.
Control systems (electrical, pneumatic, others).
Telephone/communications.

Specialist:
Process plant for food, pharmaceutical, petro-chemical, or manufacturing activities.
Security (CCTV, sensors, access control).
Facility management system.
Acoustic and vibration scans.
Lifts, escalators, others.
IT systems, eg IBM, DEC, ICL, others.

Contract documents

Responsibilities – Client/contractor/manufacturer:
Bills of quantities/activity schedule items for commissioning activity with
    separate sums or clearly worded inclusion in M&E item descriptions.
Specification of commissioning:
    provision for proving that commissioning is performed – observation, test
    results;
    methods and procedures to be used, appropriate standards/codes of practice,
    eg CIBSE/IHVE/BSRIA/IEE/LPC/BS (see Commissioning documents attached);
Provision for appropriate Client access.
Client staff training.
Operating and Maintenance Manuals (as installed).
Statutory approvals.
Record drawings and equipment software (as installed) and test certification.
Statutory approvals (lifts, fire protection, others).
Insurance approvals.

Contractor's commissioning programme

Manufacturers' works testing.
Site tests prior to commissioning (component testing, eg a fan motor).
Pre-commissioning checks (full system, eg air conditioning by contractor before demonstration to Client).
Set to work (system by system).
Commissioning checks (including balancing/regulation).
Demonstration to Client (system basis).
Performance testing (including integration of systems).
Post commissioning checks (including environmental fine tuning during facility occupancy).

APPENDIX E COMMISSIONING DOCUMENTS

CIBSE

Commissioning Codes

A	Air distribution
B	Boiler plant
C	Automatic control
R	Refrigerating systems
W	Water distribution systems
TM12	Emergency lighting

BSRIA

TM 1/88	Commissioning HVAC systems, divisions of responsibilities
TN 1/90	European commissioning procedures
AG 1/91	The commissioning of VAV systems in buildings
AG 2/89	The commissioning of water systems in buildings
AG 3/89	The commissioning of air systems in buildings
AG 1/89	Flushing and cleaning of water systems

HMSO

HTM 17	Health building engineering installations, commissioning and associated activities
HTM 82	Fire safety in health care premises, fire alarms and detection systems
PSA/DOE	AC design applied to computer installations
(M&E) No. 1	Electrical installations
(M&E) No.100	Air conditioning, cooling and mechanical ventilation

OSS Prevention Council

LPC	Rules for automatic sprinkler installations

IEE

Wiring Regulations

British Standards

BS 5839	Fire detection and alarm systems for buildings
BS 5655	Lifts and service lifts
BS 5720	Code of Practice for mechanical ventilation and air conditioning in buildings
BS 7258	Laboratory fume cupboards
BS 6651	Lighting protection
BS 5266	Emergency lighting
CP 1021	Code of Practice for cathodic protection

IT

Cabling installation and planning guide of relevant 'equipment' manufacturer/supplier

APPENDIX F HANDOVER CHECKLISTS

Handover *procedure*	Architect's certificate. Certificate of Practical Completion. inspections and tests. copies of certificates, approvals and licenses. final clean. handover of spares.
Programme	remedial works. adjustment of building services. Client's fitting out.
Building *Owner's Manual*	consultants' contributions. format.

Operating and maintenance manuals and as-built and installed drawings

Letting or *disposal*	programme. publicity. strategy. liaison. documentation. insurance.
Additional works	contracts. major services installations or adaptations. fitting out. shop fitting.

Final account

Liaison with tenants, purchaser or financier

Access by *contractors*	remedial works. additional contracts.
Security	key cabinet. key schedule.

Spares

Read meters

Publicity

Opening arrangements

Client's acceptance of building

HANDOVER CHECKLISTS continued

INSPECTIONS AND CERTIFICATES

Fire Officer
inspections
fire shutters.
fireman's lift.
smoke extract system/pressurisation.
foam inlet/dry riser.
fire dampers.
alarm systems.
alarm panels.
telephone link.
fire protection systems.
— sprinklers.
— hose reels.
— hand appliances/blankets etc.
statutory signs.

Fire Certificate

Institution of Electrical Engineers' Certificate

Water Authority certificate of hardness of water

Insurer's
inspections
fire protection systems.
— sprinkler.
— hose reels.
— hand appliances.
lifts/escalators.
mechanical services.
— boilers.
— pressure vessels.
— electrical services.
— security installations.

Officers of the Court Inspection (licensed premises)

Pest control specialists' inspection

Environmental Health Officer inspection

Building Control Officer inspection

Planning
outline.
detailed including satisfaction of conditions.
listed building.

Landlord's inspection

Health and Safety Officer's inspection

Crime Prevention Officer's inspection